NEW LESSONS
IN LIP READING

Based on Edward B. Nitchie's
LIP-READING PRINCIPLES AND PRACTISE

BY

ELIZABETH HELM NITCHIE
(Mrs. Edward B. Nitchie)

J. B. LIPPINCOTT COMPANY
Philadelphia and New York

To the Memory of Edward B. Nitchie

CONTENTS

Section I

FOR THE STUDENT AND HIS FRIENDS
By Edward B. Nitchie

Section II

FOR THE TEACHER

Section III

LESSON MATERIAL

Lesson Units:

Each unit includes a lesson on a fundamental sound movement, a diphthong, double or triple consonants, and three groups of homophenous words with sentences, and a group of idiomatic expressions and adages.

Fundamental Sound Movements:

8   CONTENTS

SUPPLEMENTARY MATERIAL:

MUSIC

The ruder strains of music are denied,
The music of the human voice is lost,
The gulf of silence ever grows more wide,
My bark sails noiseless o'er life's swelling tide,
    By soundless billows tost.

But waves of harmony forever roll,
Orchestral cadences e'er fall and rise:
The mysteries of the part within God's whole,
The eternal whisperings of the Over-Soul
    Still 'trance me to the skies.

Ceaseless I hear the God of Nature call
Where green and gold chant anthems in the wood;
The meadows, daisy-capped, the silver ball
Of evening, star and surging ocean—all,
    All sing of Love and Good.

It is the symphony of symphonies
Within my soul I hear,—to live, to work,
To turn my back on stumbling yesterdays,
Soul-sure, defeats may e'en be victories
    If e'er I fight, nor shirk.

                      EDWARD B. NITCHIE

FOREWORD

Since the publication of the 1930 revision of Edward B. Nitchie's *Lip-Reading Principles and Practise* much progress has been made in the field of teaching lip reading, and *New Lessons in Lip Reading* has been written to meet the need of teachers for new material developed according to present-day methods. These lessons have been based on Mr. Nitchie's book, and his general plan and his principles have been followed, but practically all lesson material is new. It has been stated often that Mr. Nitchie was ahead of his time in developing some of the principles which he applied to teaching lip reading, and we find that today his principles are in line with the latest being used in teaching reading to children and in teaching foreign languages. As early as 1908 Mr. Nitchie used dialogues and skits, and during the last year of his life he was considering developing motion pictures for home study on the part of those who live too far from a teacher to have expert instruction. He believed the time was coming when films could be rented and the cost of a projector would be within the reach of anyone with a moderate income. He was then discussing the problem with a motion picture company now out of existence.

The two articles by Mr. Nitchie—"To the Friends of the Deaf" and "The Eye as a Substitute for Deaf Ears"—have been included in their entirety. Although they were originally published in the *Volta Review* a good many years ago, they are still pertinent and helpful.

My aim in preparing this material has been to make all sentences *conversational*—the kind of sentences that are to be

13

met with in everyday intercourse—using words in their different meanings, idiomatic expressions, clichés, and adages, as they make up so large a part of our conversation, and to be familiar with them makes understanding conversation easier; to increase the vocabulary of the student where the need is indicated; and to include as wide and varied subjects as possible. It is obvious that when one does not know the meaning of some words and expressions used and is unfamiliar with the subject under discussion, understanding the speaker is much more difficult and even may be impossible.

The lesson material in this book has been prepared for use with all classes of students with defective hearing, or those who are totally deaf, in high schools, colleges, universities, audiological clinics, and schools for the deaf.

Many helpful criticisms and suggestions were received from Miss Elizabeth Brand, Miss Helen Scriver, Miss Ruth Bartlett, Miss Gertrude Torrey, Mrs. Mary Lou Rush, Mrs. Ethel L. Turley, Miss Jean Closser, and Mrs. Edna K. Monsees, to whom the manuscript, or pages of each section, were sent. The manuscript has been greatly improved by following the suggestions of these teachers, and it is with gratitude that I acknowledge my indebtedness to them for the help they gave.

Miss Mary E. Newlee and Miss Esther C. Howes carefully reviewed the manuscript and analyzed it for the publishers and they, as well as I, are deeply indebted to them for the time given to it and for the painstaking study they made of the manuscript and for the detailed report of their findings.

Elizabeth Helm Nitchie.

SECTION I

FOR THE STUDENT AND HIS FRIENDS

By Edward B. Nitchie

TO THE FRIENDS OF THE DEAF

IT IS NOT easy to be deaf; it is a mighty hard thing; and it is often made harder for us by the unnecessary friction between us and our friends arising from the fact of our deafness. That is why I ask you, the friends of the deaf, to consider some of the ways and means by which you can help to make our lot easier for us. I do not mean to scold or find fault, but to help— to help you to help us. If at times I speak plainly, even bluntly, I trust you will pardon it in view of my purpose.

If it is a question of blame, we ourselves must assume our share of it. It is often our attitude that makes things hard for both you and us. For one thing, we are prone to be too sensitive. And yet that is the most natural thing in the world. I suppose every man or woman who carries a physical affliction is more or less sensitive. The lame man, the blind man, the humpback, the stammerer, all have a fellow feeling in this regard. But the peculiarity of deafness is that it has the unhappy faculty of drawing down ridicule upon its victim.

If a lame man stumbles and falls, nobody laughs; everybody rushes to help him to his feet. If a blind man runs into a stone wall, every one is all sympathy. But let a deaf man make a mistake, due to his deafness, and everybody laughs. Yes, I know they do not laugh at him; they laugh at his mistake. If it were only easy for him to realize that, it would save him intense mortification. I suppose there is not one of us who has not felt at some time or other that he wished the floor would open and swallow him up.

When I was at college, one of the members of the glee club

17

was very bald; but he wore a wig. At the concerts he sang a
solo:

> "I'd rather have fingers than toes,
> I'd rather have eyes than a nose;
> And as for my hair,
> I'm so glad it's all there,
> I'll be sore as can be when it goes."

And with the last word he would snatch the wig from his
head. Of course everybody laughed; but the point is, that
he laughed with them. If we who are deaf would cultivate
the saving grace of laughing at our mistakes, it would take all
the sting out of them.

On the other hand, there is the danger that those who laugh
at us may get the worst of it themselves. John Wanamaker tells
the story of a deaf man named Brown, who was disposed to
stinginess.

"He never married, but he was very fond of society, so one
day he felt compelled to give a banquet to the many ladies and
gentlemen whose guest he had been.

"They were amazed that his purse-strings had been unloosed
so far, and they thought he deserved encouragement; so it was
arranged that he should be toasted. One of the most daring
young men of the company was selected, for it took a lot of
nerve to frame and propose a toast to so unpopular a man as
Miser Brown. But the young man rose. And this is what was
heard by every one except Brown, who never heard anything
that was not roared into his ear:

"'Here's to you, Miser Brown. You are no better than a
tramp, and it is suspected that you got most of your money
dishonestly. We trust that you may get your just deserts yet,
and land in the penitentiary.'

"Visible evidences of applause made Brown smile with gratification. He got upon his feet, raised his glass to his lips, and said, 'The same to you, sir.' "

Inattention is one of our chief faults. Not hearing what is going on around us, we are apt to withdraw into our own thoughts; and then, when some one does speak to us, we are far away. We need to be more on the alert than others, just because we cannot hear; our quickness of eye must make up for our aural slowness. To you, our friends, I wish to make the suggestion that you draw our attention, not by touching us, not by a violent waving of the arm or perhaps the handkerchief, not by shouting to us, but by a quiet movement of the hand within our range of vision. We are sensitive. Anything that brings our affliction into the limelight of the observation of others cuts like a lash; and there are few things we dislike more than having our attention attracted by a poke or a pull, though a gentle touch is sometimes not disagreeable.

Another of our faults is a tendency to seclusiveness. We not only draw into our own thoughts when others are present; we often retire from company into the solitude of a book or magazine, or avoid company altogether. It is a rudeness, I know, to pick up a book and read when in the company of others; yet it is a rudeness that even our friends ought sympathetically to condone. And, moreover, I ask you which is the greater rudeness, that of our taking up our book or that of your passing around the sweets of conversation and offering none to us? Truly, we ought not to seclude ourselves, but we need your help.

We have our faults, and so have you, and your chief fault, as far as we are concerned, is that you do not realize what it means to be deaf. Occasionally I hear some one say he wishes he might be deaf for a little while; he would be glad if some of the disturbing noises might be eliminated. Oh, deafness is not so bad, he opines; it has its advantages—which I do not deny; but they are not the advantages he has in mind. I sometimes wish that such a person might truly be deaf for say a year without the knowledge that at the end of that time his hearing would be restored to him. Then he would find the one-time disturbing noises had become music in his ears, and that the advantages of deafness, provided he had met his affliction in the right spirit, were of a spiritual and not of a physical nature.

It is thoughtlessness, due to ignorance of conditions, that is the cause of most of the troubles between you and us. It is not selfishness—not usually, at any rate—but just that you do not stop to think. And that is why I am writing to you: to help you to understand and show the same thoughtfulness toward us as you instinctively would show toward the blind.

It is easy enough for us to imagine what lameness and what blindness mean; probably most of us have been more or less lame at some time or other, and we are all of us blind when in the dark. But it is a much more difficult thing for the hearing to imagine the full calamity of deafness. Think how much of the sweetness of life comes to you through your ears. The joys of companionship and fellowship with other men and women are dependent on our understanding what they have to say. Try for one week to imagine what it would be like if every spoken word that comes to you were lost. Think each time, "Suppose I had not heard that," and when you have finally comprehended what the world of silence is, your sympathetic understanding will go a long way toward lightening our cross.

If you could really put yourselves in our place, one of the first things you would realize is that there are few things that so irritate as to have you shout at us. It is so unnecessary and uncalled for, and makes us the center of unenvied observation. We will in fact understand you better if instead of shouting you enunciate clearly and distinctly and make your voice as vibrant as may be possible.

In a general conversation we greatly need your help. A certain deaf man expressed the unuttered view of many another when he said, "I enjoy a conversation with one person, but when a third breaks in upon us, h—— enters the room with him." In nine cases out of ten the deaf man is given no share in general conversation, and for all purposes of social enjoyment he might almost as well be marooned on a desert island.

General conversation is hard for us to understand, even though we be skillful readers of the lips. As we all know, it is very much easier to follow conversation when we know the subject. When two people are talking we may say that each has a one-half share; when three, each has a one-third share, and so on. This is true provided all can hear. But if one is deaf, while it is still true he has a half-share when only two are talking, when three are talking he has no share at all! If only the others would talk to him! But no, they talk to each other, and he is out of it. My advice to you, then, in a general conversation, is: "Talk to us." The others will hear you, and it will give us the benefit of sharing in the conversation, of knowing the subject, and of greatly increased ease of understanding.

There are times, I know, when it is not possible to talk to us, or others may be talking who have not the thoughtfulness to do so. Then what we ask of you is not to rehash the conversation after the topic has been talked out, but by a word or two at the beginning to indicate to us the subject.

The suggestions I have given you so far will apply whether we are lip-readers or not. Now I wish to give you some suggestions that will help us in our endeavor to hear with the eyes. For one thing, let the light be on your face, not on ours. It requires only a little thoughtfulness to see to this important requisite. In my own family such thoughtfulness has become so instinctive as to be a habit, and the endeavor to get the light right is always a first thought when any of the family are talking to me.

The exaggeration of the facial movements, "mouthing," usually arises on your part from the best intentions to help us understand. You mean well, but as a matter of fact you are making it harder for us. Such exaggeration throws the mouth out of all natural movement and formation, and makes it impossible for us to know just what we do see. All we ask of you is that you speak distinctly, and then the movements of your lips and tongue will take care of themselves.

Closely associated with your endeavor to help us by exaggeration is the endeavor to help through a word-by-word manner of talking. The human mind naturally takes in the thought as a whole and not piecemeal, one word at a time. It is exasperation to ask us to understand in that way. How much of the thought of this printed page would you get if you stopped to think about each word separately? Like the man who could not see the woods for the trees, so when—you—talk—this—way we cannot see the thought for the words. If it is necessary to speak slowly to us, let it be smoothly, connectedly, and not word by word.

Another of your well-meant efforts to help us consists in repeating for us a single word that we have failed to understand; it is much easier for us to get the word in its thought connection in a sentence. For the same reason, the long phrase is usually easier than the short phrase; as, for example, "Will you get me a drink of water?" presents much less difficulty than "Will you get me a drink?"

In your choice of words, try to choose if possible those that have the most movement of the lips. If you want to say "a quarter," choose the words "twenty-five cents." For "fifty cents," however, you should say "half a dollar," for not only does the latter phrase have more lip-movement, but it is also true that "fifty cents" might easily be mistaken for "fifteen cents." As another example, notice as you say the sentences how much plainer and more pronounced the lip-movements are for "What beautiful weather we are having" than for "Isn't it a nice day?"

Proper names are always hard, because we have as a rule no context to help us. When you introduce us to strangers, be careful to speak the name clearly and distinctly direct to us. Not infrequently I find my hearing friends introducing me with a decided emphasis on my own name, as though it were very necessary that I should understand that, and with the name of my new acquaintance so mumbled that I do not know whether he is Teufelsdröckh or Smith. Again, when in conversation you are referring to some one by name, a short explanatory phrase will often help us wonderfully; as, "I like to deal at Scudder and Singer's—*the meat market, you know.*"

I have presented to you some of our problems, believing that you can help us. Yet I realize that you cannot do it all—that we must coöperate. And the first thing for us to do in the way of self-help is frankly to acknowledge our deafness. I think no greater mistake can be made from the standpoint of our own comfort and peace of mind than that of trying to conceal the fact that we cannot hear. It is not only sensitiveness, it is also a feeling of shame, as though we had done some wrong, that impels us to try to hide our failing ears. We need the advice of the lunatic in the story. All day long a fisherman had been sitting on the bank of the stream and had not caught a thing. All day long the lunatic had watched him from a window in the neighboring insane asylum. At last the man in the window could endure it no longer, and he shouted to the fisherman: "Hey, there, you poor fool! Come on inside!"

So we need to come on inside the ranks to which we belong,

frankly, realizing that it is no crime to be deaf, and then try by every means in our power to make our lives normal and sane. That is what we are striving to do, and we ask your help that our burden of deafness may be lightened as much as possible.

THE EYE AS A SUBSTITUTE FOR DEAF EARS

It is well known that the blind in a measure substitute hearing for sight; sounds of traffic in a busy street are a confused roar to the untrained ear, but to the experienced blind man they are a fairly reliable guide on his way.

Even to a greater degree can the deaf man train his eye to substitute for his deaf ears.

Watch the mouth of anyone who is speaking, and you will see many clearly defined movements of the lips, perhaps even of the tongue. The eye trained to associate certain movements with certain sounds has the power of interpreting these movements into words and sentences.

A very large percentage of the deaf are, I believe, incurable, at least at the present state of medical and surgical knowledge. The greatest loss to anyone who is deaf is the loss of understanding speech. Inability to hear music or the voices of nature is a deprivation; but inability to hear spoken language is a calamity, unless other means than the ear can be found to convey the message to the brain; for in the ability to understand spoken language lies the way not only to the pleasures of life, but to the truest necessities of the soul and body.

Deafness is a physical bar to employment second only to blindness, and bears especially heavily on the man who, dependent on others for his salary, becomes deaf in adult life. Lip-reading, or speech-reading, "that subtile art," as Dr. John Bulwer said in 1648, "which may inable one with an Observant Eie to Heare what any man Speaks by the moving of his Lips," is a valuable substitute for hearing, as far as spoken language is

concerned, though, like any other substitutes, it has its limitations. By it the sense of sight is forced to interpret a medium
for expressing thought which, throughout the history of the
race, has been developed for the needs of the sense of hearing.
I shall show later how imperfectly spoken language is fitted to
the requirements of successful lip-reading.

The problem of the teacher varies according to the class of
the deaf to which his pupil belongs, for the deaf-mute's needs
are only in part the needs of the hard-of-hearing. My work lies
with the hard-of-hearing—and by that term I mean those who,
either partly or totally deaf, became so after having acquired
speech and language—and it is of their problem of which I
shall speak particularly. It is not only their problem; its solution becomes also the solution of the problem of the deaf-mute
after he acquires speech and language.

The problem of teaching lip-reading is truly a psychological
problem. Both the eyes and the mind must be trained, but
mind-training is the more important factor.

The difficulties for the eyes to overcome are two: first, the
obscurity of many of the movements, and second, the rapidity
of their formation. That spoken language is not well adapted
to the purpose of lip-reading is evident from the many sounds
that are formed within the mouth or even in the throat. The
difference between vocal and non-vocal consonants is invisible
to the eye. The aspirate *h*, as in "hat," cannot be seen; there
is no visible difference between "hat" and "at." The consonants
formed by the back of the tongue and soft palate, *k*, hard *g*, *ng*,
are seldom revealed to the eye of the lip-reader; likewise, certain tongue consonants, as *t*, *d*, *n*, and *y*, present almost in-
superable difficulties. Double tongue consonants, as *nt*, *nd*, *lt*,
ld, are also just as indefinite and obscure in their visible formation.

Rapidity of the movements is another serious difficulty in

the way of successful lip-reading. From one-twelfth to one-thirteenth of a second is the average time per movement in ordinary speech. This is the average, but some movements are of course slower, while others, particularly those for unaccented syllables, are much quicker.

With such difficulties as these, the wonder is that anyone can read the lips at all. Eye-training can never eliminate them, though it can lessen them in a measure. The method should aim first always to study or see the movements in words or sentences, not formed singly by themselves. Sounds pronounced singly all tend to be exaggerated, and many of them even to be grossly mispronounced. Moreover, one movement often modifies decidedly the appearance of another connected with it in a word. For example, long *e* usually tends to show a slight drawing back of the corners of the mouth, as in "thief"; but, after *sh,* as in "sheep," this is scarcely visible.

In the second place the method should aim always to study or see the movements as the words are pronounced quickly. It is true that it would be easier to see them when spoken slowly, but it is also true that to produce the best results the eye should be trained from the first to see things as they must always be seen in ordinary speech, and that is rapidly.

And, in the third place, the method should aim to inculcate a nearly infallible accuracy and quickness of perception of the easier movements, leaving to the mind in large measure the task of supplying the harder movements.

With the eye thus trained it often happens that the lip-reader's impression is that of actually hearing what is said. If I put the tubes of a phonograph into my ears, so that I can hear every word, and close my eyes, unbidden and without conscious effort the vision of the moving lips of the speaker forming the flow of the words passes before my mind.

Although it is not possible for the eye to see each and every movement, it is possible for the mind to grasp a complete impression without even the consciousness that it has "supplied" so many of the movements and sounds. The chief difficulties in the way of the mind in lip-reading may be indicated by describing that type of mind which is uniformly most successful, and that is a mind which is quick to respond to impressions, or quick in its reaction time, and a mind in which the synthetic qualities are dominant. The difficulties, then, are to overcome the opposite conditions or tendencies, and the aim is to develop the mind to the utmost along the line of these favoring conditions.

Fortunately thought is quicker than speech. Testing myself with a selected passage that I know by heart it takes me fifteen seconds to think of it word by word, and thirty-five seconds to read it aloud. To develop quick perception, *practice* is the essential; that is, slow speech, word-by-word utterance, must be avoided, and all forms of exercise must be given to the pupil up to the limit of speed which his ability will allow. This undoubtedly makes the work harder for the time being but it results in more rapid progress.

Not only is thought quicker than speech; thought need not formulate every word to have clear conceptions. Thought skips; thought looks ahead and anticipates. So that a correct understanding of an idea is possible without a word-for-word accuracy. That is the way the baby understands what is said to him. I would say to my little boy, when a year and a half old, "How does daddy shave himself in the morning?" That he understood every word was not possible; probably "daddy" and "shave" were the only ones he really knew. But that he understood what I said he made evident when he went through the motion of shaving his own face with his finger.

The method of mind-training should aim to develop this power of grasping thoughts as wholes, and to avoid strictly anything that will enhance the opposite tendency of demanding verbal accuracy before anything is understood at all. Minds of the latter type are literal, analytical, unimaginative. Yet there are very few who are altogether of this kind; most of us, however analytical, have some synthetic powers, some ability of putting things together, of constructing the whole from the parts, of quick intuition. It is by developing these powers that real success in lip-reading can be attained, and it is by working along these lines that the surest way is found in the end to the understanding of every word. Even those who hear, often have an experience like this: Some one will make a remark which you fail to understand; the word "what" is on your lips, but before it is fairly uttered the whole sentence will come to you like a flash. When this intuitive, synthetic power is highly developed, the "natural-born" lip-reader is the result.

I feel sure, from what is known of the men, that Prescott, the historian, would have easily learned lip-reading, while the analytical Bancroft would have found it much more difficult; that Seton Thompson would be quick to master it, and that John Burroughs would be slower; that Roosevelt would be an expert, and that Hughes would be a novice. I have repeatedly found among my pupils that those who can play music readily at sight are apt in reading the lips, for such ability implies quick reaction time and the intuitive mind.

What degree of skill can a lip-reader expect to attain? How long does it take? These are natural questions, but cannot be answered categorically. What some can attain in three months, others cannot acquire short of a year; and the highest degree of skill, as in any art, is open only to the few. But three lessons a week for three months will, with most pupils, give a very satisfactory and practical skill. I may be pardoned if I speak of myself. I can sometimes understand a lecture or sermon, depending upon conditions of light, etc.; less often can I understand a play. I am called a good lip-reader, but I know better ones. With a very few exceptions, such a degree of skill is possible to every one as to make home life and social friendships a joy once more, and, though it may not be an infallible resource in business, it may for all be an invaluable aid. Lip-reading can never do all that good ears ought to do, but what it can do is almost a miracle.

Two objections to lip-reading I occasionally hear: (1) That it is too great a strain on the eyes, and (2) that, by relieving the ears from hearing, there is a tendency to deterioration in hearing from lack of exercise.

The strain upon the eyes at first is truly no small one; but I have repeatedly found that those who complain of eyestrain during their first lessons, later never think any more about it. I have not strong eyes, and now, though I use them in reading the lips every day and all day long, they are seldom overtired. If the lip-reader is careful from the first to cease using the eyes at the first symptom of tire, I believe that no harm can result and gradually the eyes will be able to do more and more.

The objection in regard to the deterioration of hearing I believe to be the reverse of true. Dr. Albert Barnes, in *The Dietetic and Hygienic Gazette,* of October, 1909, said: "People with ear strain should spare the hearing as much as possible, and, instead of straining the ear to catch what is said, they should watch the lips more. In other words, the eyes should be called upon to help the ears." Moreover, with pupils who have enough hearing to hear the sound of the voice, I advise and encourage them to use ears and eyes in fullest coöperation, one helping the other.

Under such circumstances, and also in view of the fact that the ear involuntarily gets exercise with every sound that comes to it, whether the strain to hear is made or not, I do not see how any harm can be done to the ears by lip-reading, and in all my experience I have never found any evidence of such harm. On the contrary, several times pupils have reported to me an actual betterment of the hearing, though how much lip-reading had to do with it and how much other conditions I do not pretend to say.

Lip-reading, then, is not a cure for deafness, nor is it even a cure for all the ills of deafness; but from some of the worst ills it is a true alleviation. It takes first place on the majority of occasions over all mechanical devices. For those completely deaf, or so deaf as to make mechanical devices out of the question, lip-reading is the only resource. For those whose deafness still allows them to hear the sound of the voice, it obviates the necessity of using these more or less cumbersome and inconvenient contrivances. Even at such times when these devices can be used to advantage, watching the lips helps to make them more useful and more reliable. Under any circumstances, lip-reading has in it the power to make deafness of whatever degree much easier to bear.

FOR THE TEACHER

GENERAL PRINCIPLES

THE TEACHER SHOULD keep in mind when giving the first lessons that the student is not a lip reader and, therefore, must *hear* all explanations. If the student hasn't a hearing aid of his own and none is at hand for him to use, a voice sufficiently loud to be heard must be used. If he is too deaf to hear at all, then instructions should be written, regardless of the time it may take, for unless he understands what it is all about and what is expected of him, and he has some idea why various exercises and drills are given, disappointment and unsatisfactory work, if not actual failure, are sure to follow.

On the first lesson the student should be told what we mean by lip reading and what can and cannot reasonably be expected from its study. It should be explained that so-called "lip" reading involves more than interpreting the movements of the lips. It also involves *listening* in order to make use of all hearing possible; watching facial expressions and expressions of the eyes, and gestures for clues; of using all one's mental faculties in following the trend of the conversation.

Lip reading has very definite limitations; it is a crutch for the hard of hearing, and an invaluable aid for the very deaf, but it is not an unfailing resource in time of need. Even an expert lip reader cannot possibly read lips that do not move, or the lips of a person whose mouth is badly formed and whose lip movements are unnatural. Light plays an important part in lip reading. If the speaker's back is to the light and his mouth in the shadow his lips cannot be seen distinctly or they may not be seen at all. Lips cannot be read in the dark. Fatigue interferes with good lip reading, and nervousness or nerve strain. Because of all this it is all the more necessary for a hard of hearing person to use a hearing aid. Just to hear the murmur of the conversational voice or the rhythm of speech helps in lip reading, and lip reading helps in interpreting the imperfect or blurred sounds that may come to the ears.

As the explanation of this concept of lip reading has been so clearly and ably expressed by Dr. Irene R. Ewing of the University of Manchester, Manchester, England, in her book, *Lip Reading and Hearing Aids,* I am quoting her as follows: "The old view about lip reading—that it was a substitute for hearing—was very harmful. It led some doctors and many laymen to suggest that if one learnt lip reading one's ears would become lazy. This view takes no account of the mental effort involved in successful lip reading nor does it allow for the fact that hearing and listening to speech are natural habits and part of one's everyday mental experience. They are such deeply rooted habits that normally it takes an effort of will or great preoccupation to prevent oneself from listening. One cannot by mental effort alone prevent oneself from hearing noises or sounds that are within one's range of hearing. No one suggests that a man with a wooden leg is in danger of allowing his good leg to fall into disuse. The purpose of a wooden leg is to facilitate movement and to reduce the strain on the good leg. Let us have done, once and for all, with this bogey idea which has entered the imagination of some well-meaning but mistaken advisers to deaf persons. There is another fallacy which modern knowledge about lip reading exposes. Some old-fashioned teachers of lip reading and many other people drop their voices or speak in a whisper whenever they talk to a lip reader. An unnatural feeling of conspiracy permeates this kind of conversation even if it is only about the weather. The poor lip reader is denied such sounds of voice as his filtering ears allow to pass to his brain. It would be as sensible to blindfold a man because he has bad sight. It is the sound of the voice that gives life to words. It conveys much of a speaker's personality, his mood and his emotions of the moment, over and above the meaning and implication of the words themselves. Never deny this kind of vital stimulation to a partially deaf person. Speak to him at exactly the same level of loudness as when you talk to other people. All the words and vowels that fall below the level of loudness at which we can hear will give him plenty of practice in lip reading."

As the ultimate aim of all lip reading teaching is to train a student to understand conversation, he must be trained along lines that will make such understanding reasonably easy and accurate. To do so involves training along very definite lines. One of the most important factors in training, if lip reading is to be of value in everyday contacts, is to be sure that the student who hears conversation at all, with or without a hearing aid, has some sound of the voice when taking lessons. If he is too deaf to hear any voice without a hearing aid, then have the hearing aid worn during the lesson period. All lessons need not be given so that the voice is heard, but enough should be given so that the student will form the habit of listening and lip reading at the same time. When all lessons are given so the student does not hear anything at all, there is a tendency to become confused in conversation if the voice is heard; the student must hear all, or lip read all, and cannot combine the two. The student should be urged to *think* hearing at all times, but to keep his eyes on the face of the speaker, unconsciously making use of his lip reading. Such a habit will keep the hearing more acute and train the hard of hearing person to listen to sounds around him. The teacher should use some voice at all times. Anyone speaking without any voice at all tends to exaggerate the speech movements. Even in the early days of his teaching Mr. Nitchie urged his students to "use your ears for all they are worth" at all times, and when a student had sufficient hearing to get even the murmur of the voice in conversation, he gave the lessons with just enough voice to train him to combine his hearing and lip reading.

The various exercises in the book are designed to be used in training both mind and eyes along certain lines. The teacher must know not only how to use the exercises to get the best results; she must know why she is using them and what results she expects to get from her method of giving them. Her principles should be so much a part of her that at all times she will unconsciously follow them. It isn't the exercise itself that is so important as the way a teacher adapts it to the needs of each individual, and the ends achieved. The teacher should be so familiar with the exercises that she can use them without conscious effort and so can give her undivided attention to the development of certain characteristics in her student. If it is found that the usual program for the lesson is not getting the best results and it does not seem to be suited to the particular needs of the individual, some other way of presenting the lesson should be tried. Lip reading, like any subject worth learning, requires regular, systematic lessons that have been carefully planned to give a thorough all-around training. It is a fallacy to think that just any material given in whatever manner suits the mood of the teacher, will get satisfactory results.

All work should be given in a way to prevent the formation of bad habits, as well as to build right ones, and the teacher should guard against methods that may interfere with the development of desirable habits. There should be flexibility in the application of methods while the fundamentals remain unchanged.

In the learning process, whether the study be lip reading or golf, almost invariably there comes a time when the student feels he is not making progress; that he is at a standstill and he isn't "getting anywhere." This may be fairly early in the course of instruction, or it may come later on. If the student perseveres, however, that phase is eventually passed and he goes on to success. Therefore, it seems wise to urge students of lip reading not to drop out after a few lessons. Occasionally the writer has urged a student who could afford to do it to drop the lessons for a short time and try to put the subject entirely out of his mind. In each case where this device has been tried the student has come back refreshed and with renewed enthusiasm for the lessons. In some cases he has discovered that he has been reading the lips so naturally and easily he did not realize it and had supposed he was hearing everything.

Sentence and story material should be used to develop the mental factors that are essential to success in understanding conversation. According to Mr. Nitchie, "Such development should be definite, purposeful, with a clear understanding of what those powers are and how they may be developed." Speech is too rapid and many speech sounds and words are too obscure for it to be possible for the eyes to see everything that is said, but it is possible for the mind to comprehend completely even though some words may not be seen. Therefore, the student should be trained from the first to grasp the thought as a whole. Sentence and story work will develop this power if given in the right way. The student should not be permitted to interrupt until a sentence, or a complete thought, is finished, thus training the mind to continue working instead of stopping as soon as something is not understood, for often the sentence, or the idea, will come "in a flash" before the sentence is finished. In conversation there is not time to stop and either think back or ask what has been said, and so the mind must be trained to continue to follow the speaker. Though when one really has failed to follow he should not hesitate to ask the speaker to repeat.

The power to anticipate thought, being given a clue of some kind—as the subject of the conversation, a clue word, a gesture, facial expression, etc.—should be developed. If the mind is ready there will be a quicker, more complete understanding than if the lip reader is not prepared. This power can be trained through the use of words and sentences based on the words; questions on the stories; sentences on a definite topic, and the like.

If a lip reader is to be able to follow conversation with ease, his mind as well as his eyes must be trained to work fast. Conversation is too rapid to permit the lip reader to think things out for himself, so he should have all work given him in such a way as to demand from him the quickest response possible. But it should be kept in mind that what is slow for one may be too rapid for another. One should never go beyond the student's ability in speed. Both mind and eyes can be trained to work more rapidly through various devices such as are used in remedial reading. For many years teachers have used such devices, particularly in work with children. There are machines on the market which are used for this purpose but few teachers have access to them. However, they can develop their own devices. Some teachers use flash cards of various kinds, and also pictures in which there are many details, the picture being shown for a given time and then the student being requested to name as many articles or details as possible. The teacher can develop a lesson from such a picture using her own ingenuity and varying her devices as she sees fit.

One of the most difficult things for a lip reader in a conversation is to have the subject change without warning, the speaker going off on an entirely new trend of thought. Or the conversation may be the give and take of a group, making it difficult for the lip reader to follow. Therefore, the student should be trained to be alert, ready for any change in subject or anything that may come. This ability is gained by going quickly from one sentence to another not connected in thought, or by question practice where one question is "fired" at the student and demanding a quick response.

An important factor in learning lip reading is the power to concentrate. Without concentration successful lip reading is not possible. This factor can best be developed by making the work interesting. It can be developed with every form of practice if the teacher can interest the student and hold his attention. Many people with defective hearing, particularly if it has extended over a long period of time, have lost the power to concentrate. As they have been able to hear only fragments of conversation, and listening has been a severe strain on their nervous system, they have formed the habit of thinking their own thoughts and not trying to hear what is going on around them unless it is something about which they are concerned. When this power of concentration is developed it results in actually hearing better simply because the individual is paying attention to what is being said and so is training himself to listen.

While the mental factors are all-important in lip reading training, eye training should not be neglected. Exercises designed to train the eyes to be as accurate as possible in their subconscious knowledge and recognition of sound movements and words, to speed up their work, and to acquire increased visual memory are valuable in any lip reading teaching. Occasionally the suggestion that the student see an ophthalmologist to determine if a visual defect is causing difficulty, in indicated.

There are various methods of supplementing the regular instruction, such as motion pictures, skits, and dialogues, and all of them have value. The student should be trained to read the lips of as many people as possible and under as many different conditions as possible. Miss Martha E. Bruhn pioneered in giving part of her lessons in profile and nearly all teachers today recognize its value and use the device. The writer questions the value of providing extraneous noise and distractions during the intensive lesson periods, and believes it can be harmful by preventing some students from learning to concentrate and so interfere with acquiring skill in lip reading. After one has learned to concentrate and has become a good lip reader, he will be able to lip read when there is noise and confusion. Such a device might be used with advanced students, but the writer agrees with Mr. Nitchie in his belief that during the *learning process* the student has a right to have the conditions under which he takes his lessons as nearly ideal as possible.

There are certain underlying principles which a teacher should make so much a part of his mental equipment that he cannot forget them, and they are:

1. *Be natural* in everything you do. That was the underlying principle of all Mr. Nitchie's work in lip reading. He said: "The teacher who 'mouths' or speaks word-for-word or very slowly is deviating from the natural and is doing the student positive harm rather than good. It may make the work easier for the student temporarily, but ultimate success is made more difficult. Phrases or sentences not in accord with natural speech and utterance, or in the literary style rather than the spoken style are not natural."

2. *Be thorough* in all your work, but remember that what one person may be able to see with ease another may not be able to see at all. Don't waste time trying to make a student do the impossible, but don't fail to get all the value possible from each lesson, through repetition and review.

3. *Make the work interesting*. An interested student is a student won to coöperation. Such a student will concentrate

more effectively than one whose interest is dulled. Mechanical, expressionless work on the part of the teacher is inefficient work, no matter how good the methods. The teacher should seek variety, work that stimulates the imagination, and material that has an interest of its own apart from the practice.

4. *Get the maximum values* out of all work. Lose no opportunity to get the maximum value from each exercise, remembering that there are few forms of exercise that have only a single purpose in view and that cannot be used to achieve several different beneficial results if used in the right way. A teacher who knows how to handle each form of practice so as to secure the maximum results will accomplish far more than the teacher who has a single purpose in view.

5. *Prevent the formation of bad habits.* Guard against methods that may interfere with the development of any desirable habit. The teacher should have such complete mastery of his subject that none of all the aims he is working for is obscured or blocked. Be careful not to allow the formation of habits that will interfere with successful lip reading of conversation. Rather than help over a difficult place, for instance, by speaking so slowly as to be unnatural, or enunciating with more than natural distinction, let the student have the help of memory, or some sound of the voice, or the thought in different form, for we must remember we are training him to understand conversation which is ordinarily rapid, and he should form the mental habit of following fairly rapid speech. To require verbal accuracy of all sentence work tends to develop an analytical type of mind, and it means a lost opportunity to work for alertness. It also creates a lack of confidence in the ability to understand and so interferes with successful lip reading.

6. *Seek to meet the particular needs of each student.* No two students are just alike; the weakness of one may be the strength of another, or vice versa. The teacher must know the require-

ments of each individual case and must be able so to adapt the work as to get the best results.

All of these general principles mean flexibility in applying the methods, while the fundamentals remain unchanged. The methods have a two-fold purpose, i.e., training the eyes and training the mind. These two purposes cannot be absolutely separated, nor is there any need that they should be. Nevertheless, there are certain forms of practice preëminently useful in training for the qualities the eyes should have, and others in training for the desired qualities of the mind.

The material which follows was published in 1909 by Mr. Nitchie in a *Teacher's Handbook to Lessons in Lip Reading,* and was included in the 1930 edition of *Lip Reading Principles and Practise.* It seems to be as applicable to the teaching today as when it was written so many years ago, and so it is being given: Successfully to teach lip-reading requires on the part of the teacher a two-fold ability, first to impart knowledge, second, to develop skill. Some fundamental principles of teaching, which apply to all instruction, may well be stated and should be taken closely to heart.

To Impart Knowledge

1. Show, demonstrate, to the eye whenever possible; do not merely explain.

2. Show by comparison and contrast.

3. Illustrate by examples.

4. Repeat; repeat explanations, demonstrations, illustrations; but let each repetition either add something new, or else consider the subject from a new standpoint.

To Impart Skill

5. Make the student actually do the thing that is to be done. Emphasize the practical over the theoretical.

6. Repeat, repeat, and re-repeat the process until it becomes a habit.

7. Develop quick reaction, rapidity of thought and action.

As applied to the teaching of lip-reading, these fundamental principles mean (among other things):

1. Do not merely explain and describe the movements; show the pupil on your own mouth just what the movement is.

2. Show a movement by comparison or contrast with other movements whenever possible.

3. Do not merely name a sound, e.g., short *ĕ,* but illustrate by putting it in a word, as "bet."

4. Do not be satisfied with one explanation or demonstration of a movement, but repeat in different ways until you are sure the pupil understands.

5. Spend little time in explaining the theory; spend much time in making the pupil actually read the lips, for words, for sentences, for stories, for exercises.

6. Repeat words, sentences, stories, exercises many times.

7. Give nothing very slowly, neither words nor sentences, stories or exercises, and always try to increase the speed as the ability of the pupil may allow. In anything that is to be repeated after you by the pupil, insist upon a quick response.

Study these principles of teaching, affirm them constantly, put them into practice, and grow into their spirit.

SUGGESTIONS FOR USING LESSON MATERIAL

Lɪᴘ ʀᴇᴀᴅɪɴɢ ɪs based on the movements that represent sounds (not letters) of the consonants, vowels, and diphthongs. Some movements are plainly seen and easily learned—as the movement for *p, b,* and *m*—while others are so obscure as to require help of the context for their recognition—as the movement for the sounds of *k,* hard *c,* hard *g, ng, nk,* etc. Because there are no visible movements for the sounds of *y,* long *u,* and *h,* unless speech is grossly exaggerated, there are no lessons based on these sounds as they have no drill value. However, the student will have constant unconscious practice with these sounds in all the work he does.

It is not intended that the student shall learn, or memorize, all these movements, but it is intended that he shall develop associations which translate movements into words. In developing the lessons on the movements, the aim has been to group the consonant and vowel sounds so that the maximum of value can be gained from repetition and review.

In order that Mr. Nitchie's grouping of speech sounds will be better understood, the following diagrams are given. The consonants are divided into four groups as follows:

1. Those formed and revealed by the lips.
   (a) P, b, m, mp and mb—Lips-Shut.
   (b) F and v—ph and gh—Lip-to-Teeth.
   (c) Wh and w—Puckered-Variable.
2. Those formed by the tongue and revealed by the lips.
   (a) R—Puckered Corners.

(b) S, z and soft c—Extended-Narrow.

(c) Sh, zh, ch, j, soft g—Lips-Projected.

3. Those formed and revealed by the tongue.

(a) Th—Tongue-to-Teeth.

(b) L—Pointed-Tongue-to-Gum.

(c) T, d, n, nt, nd—Flat-Tongue-to-Gum.

4. Those revealed by the context.

(a) Y—Relaxed-Narrow.

(b) K, hard c, hard g, ng and nk—Throat-Movement.

(c) H—No Movement (Aspirate).

The vowels fall into three groups, i.e., puckered, relaxed and extended, and each group has three widths of opening between the lips, narrow, medium and wide. The diagram below will make this clear.

Width of Opening	Shape of lips		
	Puckered	Relaxed	Extended
Narrow	Long ōo (coon)	Short ĭ (kid)	Long ē (keen)
Medium	Short ŏŏ (good)	Short ŭ (cut)	Short ĕ (get)
Wide	Aw (caw)	Ah (cart)	Short ă (cat)

There are two groups of diphthongs, i.e.

1. Those with a puckered final movement.

(a) Ow, as in "how." Relaxed-Wide, followed by a puckered movement.

(b) Long ō, as in "go." Contracting puckered movement.

(c) Long ū, as in "mute." Relaxed-Narrow and Puckered-Narrow.

2. Those with relaxed and narrow final movement.

(a) Long ī, as in "pipe." Relaxed-Wide and Relaxed-Narrow.

(b) Long ā, as in "late." Extended-Medium and Relaxed-Narrow.

(c) Oy, as in "boy." Puckered-Wide and Relaxed-Narrow.

On the first few lessons the teacher should explain this in a general way so that the student will have some understanding of the development of the fundamental sound movements to be studied and the value to be gained from such a study, but a detailed description of all sound movements in the first few lessons to precede the study of one at a time, has a tendency to confuse the average student who has no knowledge of the subject.

The method of learning the movements involves, first, a clear conception of their characteristics, and, second, much practice in the observation of them. The aim of the practice is to make the recognition of the sound movements an unconscious act; that is, by much repetition to make the association of certain movements with certain sounds a habit, something which we do without counsciousness of effort or concentration. All *word* exercises must be repeated, as this constant repetition helps to fix in the mind of the student the characteristics of the various movements, and there is no other way to verify the accuracy of the word repeated. Such repetition makes use of the multiple sense of appeal as the student *sees* the word on the lips of the teacher, he *hears* himself say the word, and he *feels* it as he repeats it. The kinesthetic sensation plays an important part in the training for a subconscious knowledge of the movements, without which successful lip reading is impossible.

In developing the movement words the principle adhered to throughout *Lip-Reading Principles and Practise,* which the writer has followed, is to combine with the new movement on which the lesson for the day is based, all the movements previously studied, or the last two or three, thus providing constant repetition and review, which helps to train for a subconscious knowledge of the movements. In several instances there will be a deviation from the usual order followed in developing movement words. For example, in the lesson on short *u*, relaxed-medium, short *i*, relaxed-narrow, is combined with the short *u* for drill on the difference in width of opening between the lips (almost imperceptible); then short *e, extended*-medium, is combined with the short *u, relaxed*-medium, for drill on the difference between the extended and relaxed characteristics.

In all word-practice the student should always know which words are being used, for words without context are very hard to recognize, and as this exercise is for eye training primarily, the student should have the words in mind so that his entire attention can be focused on recognizing and repeating the words in the order given. The teacher should show the particular group of words to be used and then should give these words in different order, the student repeating them in the order given. If there is great difficulty experienced by the student in repeating the words, the teacher should show them again and let the student see them on her lips, then try again to give them without his knowing the order in which they are given. When giving movement words it is well to follow the order in which they are presented in the book. For instance, on Lesson VIII, give the first group of words with *p, b,* and *m* both before and after the vowel; then *f* and *v* in the same way; and *wh* and *w,* etc., always giving the two groups—before and after the vowel —before going to the next consonant group. Systematic drill gets much better results than drill given in a haphazard manner.

The Practice Words are not in any sense a vocabulary to be learned but are intended for the purpose of word-practice as well as other forms of practice. There are several ways to study words. They may be used to train for accuracy, as when a word is given and repeated by the student; to train the mind in quickness and associated thought, as when a word is given, repeated by the student; and a sentence embodying the word is given quickly; to train for thought-getting, when sentences are used, by not permitting interruption until the sentence is completed, and by insisting on thought-getting rather than a word-for-word understanding; and to train both eyes and mind in alertness by requiring a quick response.

All forms of practice have both a definite, or obvious, purpose and one or more general purposes. The obvious purpose of working for special movements, words, or sentences, is not likely to be overlooked, but the general purposes of eye and mind training which are all-important in acquiring lip reading skill, should be kept in mind at all times.

A suggested method of using these words in a lesson, or in home practice, is for the teacher, or assistant, to give a word and have it repeated. When repeated a sentence built around that word should be given quickly. To make a practice of repeating all sentences tends to train the student to depend upon a word-for-word understanding, a habit which will interfere with conversational efficiency. In the early lessons it is often necessary to have repetition of sentences to give the student confidence in his ability to understand and to assure the teacher that he is not bluffing, but after the early lessons it is better to have the student make some response that indicates an understanding when a check is necessary. There should be some check, at least occasionally.

Another device for sentence drill is used by Miss Esther C. Howes with her high school students with great success, and with her permission I am giving it here:

The teacher selects sentences at random, and pupils respond in unison by giving only the number of each sentence. The range of selection may be limited to the first eight sentences or those sentences between twelve and twenty-four, etc.

If this rapid identification drill is given without sufficient voice to be heard by the student, pupils concentrate on the lip movements involved in a complete thought unit. If a normal speech rate is maintained, the probability of "mouthing" or of exaggerated movements is avoided. This drill should be followed by asking pupils to repeat each sentence spoken by the teacher without referring to the book.

This method will build self-confidence and avoid frustration; provide instant self-correction of faulty interpretation; establish the habit of interpreting each sentence as a unit pattern; insure the maintenance of normal speech rate and normal phrasing in all lip reading practice; and it will provide a maximum amount of correct interpretation in a given length of time.

The sentences immediately following the Practice Words use the words in the group above and are intended mainly for mind training. Simple sentences have been used almost entirely as the majority of students get better results in the early lessons, at least, with this type of material. Practically all sentences can be expanded by the teacher if her student needs practice with compound sentences. The sentences are intended to lead to conversation if conversational practice is indicated, by giving sentences associated in thought.

Sentences train the mind through insistence upon thought-getting, association of ideas, quickness of mind and eyes, visual memory (the student not being allowed to interrupt until the sentence or a complete thought is ended), and alertness because the thought changes with every sentence. One sentence should follow another as quickly as the teacher gets a response, as the practice of going from one thought to another in this way is splendid training for alertness in understanding conversation.

It will be noted that four sentences are given for each word in "Lessons on the Movements." The aim has been to use the word in different parts of speech where possible, and to provide several sentences so that one or all may be used as the teacher sees fit. While sentences should not be ungrammatical, the phrasing of colloquial language is preferred to the strictly grammatical form of written language, for it must be remembered that we are training students to understand conversation. Therefore, the conversational type of sentence has been used; that is, the kind of sentence one is likely to see in everyday conversation. And an effort has been made to give as wide a variety as possible in subject matter, and to use sentences that lend themselves to further development for continuity of thought and conversation.

A teacher should help a student with a limited vocabulary and little knowledge of things in general to gain a larger vocabulary and wider knowledge, for if one does not know the meaning of some words used and is unfamiliar with the subject, naturally conversation will not be fully understood. The larger the vocabulary and the wider the knowledge of the lip reader the more readily will he understand conversation. A teacher should not necessarily discard an exercise because it contains words that may not be understood. Rather, such words should be explained and used in sentences in as many different ways as possible so the student can add that word to his vocabulary. It requires judgment on the part of the teacher to know when she can use the exercise to increase a student's knowledge and when it should be discarded for simpler material. If sentences can be related to the interests of the student, so much the better. It has been the writer's experience that the natural, everyday expression, even though less "visible," is easier to understand than one more "visible" and less natural.

Mr. Nitchie's principles for forming sentences were: A sentence should be *natural;* it should be *colloquial,* using the spoken rather than the more formal phrasing of written language; it should contain a *complete thought-expression;* it should be *interesting;* and it should *stimulate the imagination;* that is, it should be a sentence which could lead to an expansion of the subject, as associated sentences or a bit of conversation.

To know how to use stories and other reading matter for practice we must know why we use them. In spite of the opinion held by some that "just practice" is all that is necessary, we know it is not so much the amount of practice as it is the kind of practice that produces the best results. There are right and wrong ways of doing everything, and in lip reading it is possible to practice in a way that will do absolute harm.

To develop the right habits of mind and the mental attitude that is quickest to understand conversation, stories are invaluable. Because the student is being trained in habits of mind we should use them in the way to build the right habits. It is extremely difficult for some minds to grasp thought-wholes. The fact that one student may get the thought quickly and so understand stories readily, and another may have difficulty with the stories, does not indicate that one student is more brilliant than another; it merely shows that the minds of the two students work in different ways.

The way to overcome the difficulties of the analytical mind—the one that wants to see each word—is not to allow a word-for-word understanding, but, rather, to make use of the help of memory. Some students are enabled to read thought-wholes from the lips if they have read over the material before the lesson. Far better to make use of memory help and train the mind to work in the right way, than not to use it and build bad habits.

Questions are an important part of conversation. Practice in answering questions, therefore, is essential. The questions on the stories should be natural and, at first, rather simple. The

words and phrases of the story may well be used if they make
a natural question. It is better not to have many questions that
can be answered by yes or no as the teacher cannot be sure the
questions have been understood. The questions on the following story will illustrate the type of questions that can be
asked:

ONE GOT OFF AT CLEVELAND

A traveling salesman from New England instructed the
porter on the train that he must leave at Cleveland, where he
was due at three o'clock in the morning. He explained that he
was very hard to wake up and sometimes it was necessary to
use violence to get him awake. To be sure his instructions were
carried out he gave the porter a very generous tip.

The salesman awoke at six o'clock in the morning, with
Cleveland far behind. In a rage, he sought the porter. The
colored man was in a highly disheveled state and his face was
badly bruised. His eyes popped at the sight of the furious
traveling man, who did all the talking and allowed no opportunity for the porter to make explanations or excuses. When at
last the furious salesman walked away, the porter shook his
head dismally and muttered:

"Now, ah shorely wonder who-all I done put off at Cleveland."

Questions

Where was the salesman from?
Where did he want to get off?
What time was the train due in Cleveland?
What did the salesman ask the porter to do?
What did he say might be necessary to get him awake?
How did the salesman emphasize his instructions?
What time did the salesman wake up?

Where was Cleveland?

How did he feel when he found the porter?

What was the condition of the porter?

Who did all the talking?

What did the porter say to himself as the salesman walked away?

What do you suppose the company said to the porter?

A suggested method of giving the stories is to read the story through, allowing the student to interrupt at the end of a sentence or complete thought if he has not understood. If a student has great difficulty in understanding he should be allowed to read the story to himself before this first reading by the teacher. The second step in the story program would be to read it again for verbal accuracy, once more not permitting interruption until the sentence or thought is completed. The third step would be to read it through for thought only. A fourth step would be to ask questions on the story, and if the questions are well chosen they will indicate if the student really has understood the story. A fifth step with some students would be to read the story through very rapidly without any interruption. A device for helping the student who has great difficulty in understanding a story through lip reading is to use just a murmur of voice. Often this gives all the help necessary.

From the earliest days of teaching lip reading to adults, homophenous words exercises have been considered a valuable part of the training. For those not familiar with homophenous words, it should be borne in mind that in finding homophenous words the initial and final consonant sounds must be the same, and the vowel must be the same for each word as there are no strictly homophenous sounds among the vowels, though in rapid speech long *a* and short *e* are practically impossible to distinguish except by context. Short *o* and Italian *a* (ah) differ visibly only in quantity and duration, as is also true of the *o* in "long," and broad *a* (aw). Long *u* and long *oo* are usually homophenous.

The consonants that are homophenous are:

p, b, m, mb, mp

f, v, ph, gh

wh, w

s, z, soft c

sh, zh, ch, j, and soft g

t, d, n, nd, nt, and ed following n when it does not form an extra syllable.

k, c (hard), g (hard), ng, nk, and ck.

L has no sound of like appearance and if it appears in a word it must appear in all words of the group. H is merely a breath and has no movement. Therefore, *hill* and *ill* are alike.

When making up homophenous words it must be remembered that all *sound movements,* not *letters,* must appear alike on the lips. In giving sentences using homophenous words that have more than one meaning, or are used in different parts of speech, as for example, "vault" or "smoke," they should be used in separate sentences for each meaning of the word.

The more familiar a lip reader is with homophenous words the better will he understand conversation. The ability to quickly substitute another word with the same movements when a sentence is not understood, greatly increases the ease with which a lip reader can follow conversation. One method of using homophenous words is to cover the sentences and let the student see the words in the particular group, and then give the sentences out of order so the student's mind will be ready but he will not know which word is to be used. In the groups of homophenous words in this book, proper names and obsolete words are not included as proper names are always very hard to get, and obsolete words do not lend themselves to natural, conversational sentences. It may be that every group does not include *all* homophenous words that can be found but they have been omitted intentionally.

In the lessons on Colloquial Forms, the forms given in these lessons are especially common in asking questions. The first few words of a question frequently are the key to the whole. To lose them means failure; to get them means success. The value of the repeated practice of these forms, thus fixing them in the visual memory, is therefore apparent. It is obviously good practice to train the eyes to catch the common forms and expressions which pass from mouth to mouth again and again in a day's conversation.

The Colloquial Forms questions are intended for mind training. The student knows the "form" and so has a clue and is being trained in association of ideas. If not permitted to interrupt until the question is completed, he is being trained in thought-getting, or "synthesis." If the questions are given up to the student's ability in speed, his mind and eyes are being trained to work fast, and if one question follows immediately after getting a response to the previous one, there is training for alertness.

Conversation is largely made up of idiomatic expressions and clichés, or adages, so it is well to give exercises based on such phrases and expressions. These sentences should be particularly helpful in teaching the older deaf students who have difficulty in conversation many times because they are not familiar with idioms. Be sure your student understands the meaning of all such sentences.

The Common Phrases are taken from a small pamphlet of "Common Phrases," without sentences, prepared by Edward B. Nitchie as he felt practice with such phrases as are used in everyday life would be helpful. He expected each teacher to make up her own sentences spontaneously with each lesson when used. Teachers found this difficult and rarely used these phrases. Believing, as Mr. Nitchie did, that such phrase practice has value, sentences have been prepared and are presented in this book as supplementary material.

SECTION III

LESSON MATERIAL

LESSON UNITS

Lessons on the Movements, Homophenous Words, and Idiomatic Expressions and Adages

Lesson I

P, b, m—Lips Shut

1. For *p,* as in "pie," *b,* as in "by," and *m,* as in "my," the lips open from a shut position. It is the same for each in *ordinary, rapid* speech; the sounds must be told one from the other by the context.

2.

Movement Words

peat—heap
beet—eeb
meet—deem

3.

Practice Words

meet	patch	pound
bell	moon	paid
ball	book	boat
pitch	band	burn
man	mile	point

4.

Sentences

1. Where shall I meet you for lunch?
2. We meet every day during the week.
3. We find it hard to make both ends meet.
4. I want you to meet my family before you leave.

5. I thought I heard the door bell ring.
6. The door bell must be out of order.
7. There is a loud bell on the telephone.
8. That statement rings a bell in my mind.

9. There is a ball game at the stadium today.
10. Who wants to play soft ball after school?
11. We are going to the ball park for the big game.
12. The sun was a red ball in the western sky.

13. Who will pitch in the baseball game today?
14. You can pitch the papers into the waste basket.
15. It was pitch dark when we went into the room.
16. A low-pitched voice is better over the telephone.

17. It will take a strong man to do such heavy work.
18. We must have the right man for the place.
19. The responsibilities will make a man of the boy.
20. What does the man in the street think of the election?

21. The suit will have to be patched where it was burned.
22. There is an old-fashion patchwork quilt on the bed.
23. We have a large watermelon patch on our farm.
24. There is just a patch of blue sky to be seen.

25. You are always mooning over your books.
26. The moon made everything as bright as day.
27. We are going for a moonlight ride in a hay wagon.
28. There will be a full moon tonight for our boat ride.

29. Have you finished reading the latest book?
30. I always keep a book on the table beside my bed.
31. I will have to take a leaf out of your book.
32. A mistake was made in my appointment book.

33. The band led the parade up the Avenue.
34. The neckband of the shirt is too tight.
35. The men in the band were out of step.
36. There is a steel band around the box of books.

37. "I'd walk a mile for a Camel."
38. The car broke down a mile from home.
39. We drove at the rate of a mile a minute.
40. Give him an inch and he will take a mile.

41. How much did you pay for a pound of butter?
42. The waves pound against the sides of the boat.
43. Don't pound your fist on the table when talking.
44. We get the best lobsters from the lobster pound.

45. The household bills for the month have all been paid.
46. It paid to have our plans made well in advance.
47. Were you paid well for the work you did?
48. Each one in the party paid his own expenses.

49. We have a motor boat on the river.
50. Would you like a boat ride this afternoon?
51. We made the trip to Florida by boat.
52. The boat was too crowded for our comfort.

53. You will burn your fingers on the match.
54. Money burns a hole in my pocket.
55. I let the dinner burn while I read a book.
56. The sunburn kept me awake at night.

57. The point of the pencil is broken.
58. Did you get the point of the story?
59. Will you point out the places of interest to me?
60. We missed the fine points of the story.

5.   *Homophenous Words*

Aim, ape

    What is your aim in life?

    I always aim to please my customers.

    The ape in the zoo was amusing.

    Why do you ape everything I do?

Bay, may, pay

    There is a bay window in the living room.

    Our house is only one block from the Bay.

    You may help yourself to whatever you want.

    May has been a warm month this year.

    Who will pay the bill for our purchases?

    The job does not pay enough to interest me.

Be, bee, me, pea

    Will you be home for dinner tonight?

    I think there will be rain today.

    A bee is flying around my head.

    You should keep away from the bee hives.

    I thought I heard you speak to me.

    Will you let me help you with your lesson?

    The pea vines are full of blossoms.

    We have cream pea soup for dinner.

6.   *Idiomatic Expressions and Adages*

Meet	It is hard to meet the requirements.
Pen	The pen is mightier than the sword.
Bear	I am as hungry as a bear.
Back	She never talks behind one's back.
Bacon	Be sure to bring home the bacon.
Make	We must make hay while the sun shines.
Poor	The family is as poor as a church mouse.
Man	My friend is a man of his word.

| Part | The best of friends must part. |
| Better | The family has seen better days. |

LESSON II

Long ē—Extended-Medium

7. For the sound of long *e*, as in "keen," the lips are slightly drawn back, or extended, at the corners, and the opening between the lips is narrow.

8.

Movement Words

peat—heap
beat—eeb
meet—deem

9.

Practice Words

feel	jeep	lean
wheel	beach	lease
feast	piece	reach
leaf	leap	reel
seal	mean	beef

10.

Sentences

1. Do you feel a draft from the window?
2. I like to feel the wind on my face.
3. We feel for the people who were in the flood.
4. I have the "feel" of the work at last.

5. What is the wheel base of your car?
6. The wheel of our new car is very stiff.
7. The farmer uses a wheelbarrow around the barn.
8. The patient went to his room in a wheel chair.

9. "Enough is as good as a feast."
10. We had a regular feast at the school picnic.
11. I like to feast my eyes on the beautiful view.
12. It is either a feast or a famine at our house.

13. You must turn over a new leaf January first.
14. We will have to put an extra leaf in the table.
15. Do you know what kind of leaf this is?
16. Please don't turn down the leaf in the book.

17. Be sure to seal the letter before mailing it.
18. You must have a seal on the document.
19. We watched the trained seals perform.
20. We sealed the jelly glasses with paraffin.

21. Would you like to take a ride in my jeep?
22. It was rough riding to camp in the jeep.
23. Does that truck carry a jeep inside?
24. The jeep went over the obstructions in the road.

25. We ate our picnic supper on the beach.
26. I like to lie on the beach in the sun.
27. Why did you have to beach the boat?
28. We like to spend our summers at the beach.

29. We had to piece out the material.
30. Did you like the piece of poetry I read?
31. Would you like me to walk a piece with you?
32. You can make more money doing piece work.

33. You will have to leap over the puddle.
34. We watched the salmon leap the falls.
35. The children like to play leap frog.
36. The boys like to leap over the stone fence.

37. What do you mean by that statement?
38. I didn't mean to make trouble for you.
39. We have had mean weather for the last month.
40. Did you mean to leave your books at home?

41. You may lean on me when you get tired.
42. Lean the umbrella against the wall.
43. There is not much lean meat on the roast.
44. These have been lean years for many workers.

45. You will have to sign a two-year lease.
46. I feel as if I had a new lease on life.
47. We had to lease the house for three years.
48. Do you know anything about Lend Lease?

49. Everything in the house seems to be out of reach.
50. Some people have a very long reach.
51. Will we reach home before breakfast?
52. I hope we will reach the station before the train leaves.

53. The movie is just one reel long.
54. Can you dance the Virginia reel?
55. You should reel in the fish more slowly.
56. The whole line of soldiers reeled from fatigue.

57. Will you have your beefsteak rare or well done?
58. Some people "beef" about everything that happens.
59. Beef is sometimes hard to find in the stores.
60. Shall we have roast beef or lamb for dinner?

11.   *Homophenous Words*

Sea, see

The sea is very calm this morning.
We went deepsea fishing while at the Shore.

May I see you home after the party?

Can you see the bird on the branch?

Meal, peal, peel

When do we have the next meal?

The bread is made with white cornmeal.

I am sure I heard a peal of thunder.

We can hear the peal of the church bells.

Do you like to eat the peel of the apple?

We sliced the orange peel for marmalade.

Beat, beet, meat, meet, peat

Why do you beat around the bush?

The policeman is walking his beat.

The beet is as sweet as sugar.

The sugar beet has a white root.

What kind of meat will you have?

Our family eats a great deal of meat.

We can meet after work for a game of golf.

We will meet the family on the way home.

There are peat beds in the Middle West.

Peat is used for fuel in many places.

12.	*Idiomatic Expressions and Adages*
Seat	Why did you keep me on the anxious seat so long?
Beans	Why does someone always have to spill the beans?
Bee	We made a bee line for home when we saw the storm coming.
Wheel	Everyone will have to put his shoulder to the wheel.
Steal	So you would steal a march on me!
Feel	I feel that someone has set a trap for me.
Leave	You may take it or leave it as you please.
Means	We must study ways and means to solve the problem.

Read   The boy learned to read by leaps and bounds.
Teeth   You will have to take the bit between your teeth.

LESSON III

Short ĕ—Extended-Medium

13. For the sound of short *e,* as in "get," the lips are slightly extended at the corners, and the opening between the lips is neither narrow nor wide, but medium.

14.   *Movement Words*

peat pet—heap hep
beet bet—eeb eb
meet met—team hem

15.   *Practice Words*

mend	led	west
bell	melt	shelf
fell	tell	chest
well	felt	rent
rest	sell	sense

16.   *Sentences*

1. Someone should mend the broken fence.
2. You will have to mend your ways.
3. There is never time to mend my clothes.
4. The hospital said the patient is on the mend.

5. The farmer likes to hear the dinner bell.
6. I like to hear the church bells in the country.
7. The telephone bell has been ringing for five minutes.
8. We found the cow when we heard her bell.

9. I fell for the salesman's talk.
10. A tree fell on the house in the storm.
11. The paper said prices fell last week.
12. I fell on the slippery walk after the storm.

13. There is an artesian well on the place.
14. It would be well to start for home before dark.
15. We are well on our way with the work.
16. You have done the work very well.

17. A change of work will rest you.
18. You may have the rest of the day off.
19. When do the teachers have a rest period?
20. I'll tell you the rest of the story tomorrow.

21. Who led the Marine band in the parade?
22. The President led the grand march at the ball.
23. The boy led his class in mathematics.
24. We led a quiet life in the North Woods.

25. The story you told would melt a heart of stone.
26. It was so hot in the sun I thought I would melt.
27. You should melt the butter before making the sauce.
28. The ice in the river will melt rapidly in this weather.

29. Your friend tells a story unusually well.
30. I am ready to work if you will tell me what to do.
31. I won't tell anyone what you have just told me.
32. I am willing to have you tell the news to anyone you see.

33. The sun felt warm on my face as we walked.
34. This weather is too warm to wear a felt hat.
35. I felt just like going for a long walk.
36. I felt sure you would decide to come with us.

37. How much do oranges sell for in the market?
38. This seems to be a good time to sell the house.
39. You should not sell your services too cheaply.
40. We were able to sell out the entire stock.

41. We have been watching the sun go down in the west.
42. We are building a house on the west side of town.
43. The prevailing wind in the summer is from the west.
44. How long do you expect to stay in the West?

45. You can reach the top shelf with a stepladder.
46. There are jams and jellies on the shelf in the pantry.
47. Someone should put the books back on the shelf.
48. The book is on the next to the top shelf of the bookcase.

49. Pirates buried their treasure in a chest.
50. The girls are buying things for their hope chest.
51. The athlete is proud of his chest expansion.
52. We should all contribute to the Community Chest.

53. It is time for the landlord to reduce our rent.
54. We would like to rent a cottage at the beach.
55. We pay our rent on the first of the month.
56. The dispute rent the club into two groups.

57. I can't make sense out of what you are saying.
58. She hasn't the sense she was born with!
59. All you need is plenty of common sense.
60. A sense of humor is a great help at all times.

17.   *Homophenous Words*

Elm, helm, help

There is a large elm tree in front of the house.
There is a blight on the elm trees this year.

You may take the helm of the boat for a while.

Who is at the helm of the company?

How much help will you need to finish the work?

We couldn't help ourselves under the circumstances.

Lead, led, lend, lent, let

Do you have a soft lead pencil?

A lead pipe is too soft to use for that purpose.

Who led the discussion at the meeting?

We led the life of Riley while at camp.

How much money can you lend me?

The Library will lend the book for two weeks.

I lent my name for the campaign.

We lent some equipment for the bazaar.

Will you let your house for the summer?

We let the children play in the basement.

Cent, said, scent, send, sent, set

The book you are reading isn't worth a cent.

We still pay one cent for a postal card.

You said the same thing once before.

The paper said it would rain today.

The scent of roses filled the air.

The dogs followed the scent of the fox.

Why don't you send the children outdoors to play?

You should send the package by messenger.

We sent out for more food for the company.

Everyone was sent home from the office early.

Someone should set a time for the meeting.

We haven't set eyes on you for a long time.

18. *Idiomatic Expressions and Adages*

Penny   The tramp hasn't a penny to bless his name.

Men   You'll have to wait for dead men's shoes in that company.

End	Both countries will fight to the bitter end.
Wet	Why do you throw a wet blanket over our plans?
Feather	The prize was a feather in your cap.
Few	Fame and fortune are only for the few.
Heaven	We moved heaven and earth to get the information.
Peg	That man is a square peg in a round hole.
Best	You will have to make the best of a bad bargain.
Eggs	You should not put all your eggs in one basket.

Lesson IV

Short ă—Extended-Wide

19. For the sound of short *a,* as in "cat," the lips are slightly extended at the corners, and the opening between the lips is the *widest* of the extended vowels.

20.   *Movement Words*

peat pet pat—heap hep hap
beat bet bat—eeb ebb ab
meet met mat—team hem ham

21.   *Practice Words*

path	band	cash
fast	pass	land
ran	latch	catch
sap	match	rang
lamp	fan	stamp

22.   *Sentences*

1. Where will this path take me if I follow it?
2. I could hear you as you came up the gravel path.

3. There is a well-worn path from the door to the road.
4. You should not follow the path of least resistance.

5. You talk too fast for me to understand what you say.
6. I want to take a fast train going home if I can.
7. Be sure to make the boat fast to the dock before leaving.
8. We were going too fast to stop the car at once.

9. The children ran wild all summer on the farm.
10. We ran two blocks to catch the bus and missed it.
11. We ran out of food over the weekend at camp.
12. The children ran footraces at the school picnic.

13. It is time to collect the sap for maple sugar.
14. This weather is perfect to make the sap run in the trees.
15. I am afraid the work will sap your strength.
16. The soldiers had sap lines running in every direction.

17. We always keep a lamp in the front window.
18. The floor lamp gives a better light for reading.
19. You should have a lamp with a three-way light.
20. The lamp on the hall table gives a soft glow.

21. The school band played in the Boy Scout parade.
22. You should put a rubber band around the papers.
23. The band on the motor is almost worn out.
24. We must band together if we want to succeed.

25. You should pass the car ahead on the left.
26. We drove through the pass in the mountains.
27. I hope you will pass the examination with high honors.
28. You would be foolish to pass up the opportunity.

29. I carry an extra latch key in my handbag.
30. Be sure to latch the door when you leave the house.
31. The latch string is always hanging out for you.
32. Someone should mend the latch on the back door.

33. There will be a boxing match at the club tonight.
34. Have you ever tried to match black or white?
35. The chess players are supposed to be well matched.
36. Some people have a large collection of matches.

37. Do you like to use a fan in hot weather?
38. How many fan letters have you received?
39. There is a strong draft from the electric fan.
40. The fan in the engine keeps the motor cool.

41. Do you think the bank will cash a check for me?
42. You should get a receipt if you pay in cash.
43. We buy our groceries at a cash and carry store.
44. You may take some money from the cash drawer for carfare.

45. The airplane was forced to land in an open field.
46. How much land do you own on this side of town?
47. The fertile land on the farm is very valuable.
48. The boat will land its passengers in the morning.

49. We must catch the five o'clock train if possible.
50. I am sure the door didn't catch when you closed it.
51. I tried for an hour to catch your eye at the meeting.
52. I don't want you to let me catch you doing that again.

53. I rang the doorbell but no one came to the door.
54. The neighborhood boys rang the bell and ran away.

55. I was sure the phone rang just as I came into the room.

56. The church bell rang a few minutes ago and we must leave.

57. If your feet are cold stamp them to get them warm.

58. The letter doesn't have to have an airmail stamp.

59. Will the play have the stamp of your approval?

60. How many stamps has the Post Office issued?

23.   *Homophenous Words*

Bass, mass, pass

 We went fishing in the lake for bass.

 Is this an open season for bass?

 Did you go to Mass this morning?

 There is a mass of mail to be read.

 The road was too narrow to pass the car.

 Come to see us when you pass through town.

Lamb, lamp, lap

 We had roast lamb and mint jelly for dinner.

 The children have a pet lamb to play with.

 Put your chair under the floor lamp.

 This lamp gives a very poor light.

 The boys have finished the first lap of the race.

 Those people live in the lap of luxury.

Cab, camp, cap, gap

 There is a cab stand at the corner.

 You will have to take a cab to the station.

 We had to camp out for the night.

 The Army camp was two miles from town.

 That story will cap the climax.

 Be sure to put the cap back on the bottle.

 There is a wide gap in the fence.

 We went through the gap in the mountains.

24. *Idiomatic Expressions and Adages*

Bad   The company is in a bad way.

Fat   The fat is in the fire and it is too late.

Cat   Why did you let the cat out of the bag?

Hand   The mother is tied hand and foot to the house.

Land   The land was flowing with milk and honey.

Sands The sands of time are running out.

Salary That salary is not to be sneezed at.

Cap   You will have to put on your thinking cap.

Castles We have been building castles in the air.

Manner His free and easy manner was very pleasing.

LESSON V *teach it*

F, v—Lip-to-Teeth

25. For *f*, as in "few," and *v*, as in "view," the center of the lower lip touches the upper teeth.

26. *Movement Words*

beet feet—heap heave

pen fen—ebb eff

bat vat—hap have

27. *Practice Words*

farm	form	fade
foot	fight	fall
life	safe	fire
fare	view	form
fine	voice	half

28. *Sentences*

1. We bought an abandoned farm of fifty acres.

2. The farm is only five miles from a large market.

3. The farm house has all the modern conveniences.
4. Would you like to work on the farm during vacation?

5. This is perfect weather for the big football game.
6. Which one of us is to foot the bill for lunch?
7. I am footsore and weary from Christmas shopping.
8. Can you foot up the column of figures for me?

9. There were no signs of life on the place.
10. We live the simple life when in the country.
11. Your friend was the life of the party on the trip.
12. I had to take my life in my hands on the mountain.

13. The fare on the railroad is much too expensive.
14. We are tired of the fare at this restaurant.
15. I am sure you will fare better in a warm climate.
16. There were three other fares in the taxicab.

17. We are going to have a fine day for our trip.
18. The driver paid a traffic fine of five dollars.
19. The fine type made the book too hard for me to read.
20. Our neighbor seems to be a fine type of man.

21. The parade has begun to form along Fifth Avenue.
22. I like to be allowed to form my own opinions.
23. The line at the parcel post window forms on the right.
24. The baseball team is in unusually fine form this year.

25. We had to fight for our lives in the mob.
26. The school prize was not worth fighting for.
27. We watched the prize fight on the television.
28. You will have to learn to fight your own battles.

29. It is better to play safe and be alive!
30. That rough road is not safe for traffic.
31. The money was put in the safe for the night.
32. May I leave the package with you for safe-keeping?

33. I have a long vacation in view this summer.
34. You should view the picture from a greater distance.
35. The driver had a clear view of the road all the way.
36. We would like you to give us your view of the subject.

37. Can you hear the sound of my voice so far away?
38. Her voice carried to the back of the large room.
39. Will you voice an opinion on the subject for us?
40. We would like you to have a voice in the discussion.

41. Will the dress material fade when washed?
42. We watched the light fade out of the western sky.
43. I am afraid the flowers will fade in this hot room.
44. The voice on the radio fades out now and then.

45. Be careful not to fall down the slippery steps.
46. I like the fall of the year the best of the seasons.
47. The paper says the temperature will fall tonight.
48. The waterfall is over three hundred feet high.

49. Everyone sat around the campfire and told stories.
50. There is a roaring fire in the livingroom fireplace.
51. The boy was fired with an ambition to succeed.
52. The diamond in your ring has a great deal of fire.

53. The Post Office gave us the wrong form to fill out.
54. What form of government would be best for this town?

55. The swimmer is in splendid form for the school meet.
56. You form the words unusually well on your lips.

57. Wait until you have heard the other half of the story.
58. I was interrupted when half through the work.
59. We had to live in half of a two-family house.
60. We have to walk half a mile to the mail box.

29.   *Homophenous Words*

Firm, verb

    You should be firm but kind with the children.

    The firm has changed its name and policy.

    You used the wrong verb in the sentence.

    Every sentence must have a noun and a verb.

Falls, false

    Have you been to Niagara Falls this winter?

    The hard work of the office falls on one man.

    The newspaper printed a false report of the accident.

    The box has a false bottom to keep valuables.

Face, faze, phase, vase

    We came face to face with a friend on the street.

    Be sure to face the light when speaking to a lip reader.

    The hard work and long hours did not faze him.

    You cannot faze him by arguing with him.

    That is only one phase of the subject to be discussed.

    Which phase of the moon is best for planting a garden?

    There is a vase of fresh flowers on the table.

    You should find a larger vase for the bouquet.

30.   *Idiomatic Expressions and Adages*

Face	You will have to face the music sometime.
False	You should not try to sail under false colors.
Vine	It is good to have our own vine and fig tree.

Voice	We all want a voice in the matter of organization.
Fall	I hope I am not riding for a fall.
Feet	We should stand on our own feet when possible.
Fly	There is always a fly in the ointment.
Vain	She is as vain as a peacock.
Family	Is your friend a family man?
Fence	Some politicians are always on the fence.

LESSON VI

Wh, w—Puckered-Variable

31. For *wh,* as in "what," and *w,* as in "wet," the lips are drawn together or puckered; the degree of puckering is variable, being greater in slow and careful speech, and less in rapid colloquial utterance. The sounds of *wh* and *w* occur only before vowels.

32.   *Movement Words*

bee fee wee
pen fen when
pack fag whack

33.   *Practice Words*

well	wire	watch
wait	wash	wide
wish	wind	walk
white	warm	wood
way	word	wade

34.   *Sentences*

1. The oil well made a fortune for the family.
2. It would be well for you to look over the report.
3. Are you well enough to make the trip with us?
4. If I were you I would let well enough alone.

5. Wait for me until I finish this work.
6. Did you ever wait on table at a church supper?
7. We missed the train and had a long wait for another.
8. Why did you wait so long before writing to me?

9. If wishes were horses beggars might ride.
10. I wish you would come back to see us soon.
11. The children always want the chicken's wishbone.
12. Did you ever make a wish on the new moon?

13. The field is planted with white clover.
14. Everyone wears white in the tropics to keep cool.
15. Her face was as white as a sheet when she came in.
16. There is a white picket fence around the back yard.

17. You can't expect to have everything your own way.
18. We went home by way of the Post Office for the mail.
19. The little girl has a way with her that is charming.
20. Where there is a will one can usually find a way.

21. The entire house has been wired for electricity.
22. I will wait for you to wire me before leaving.
23. The telephone wires are all down in the storm.
24. The wire on the lamp is too short to reach the socket.

25. There is a washout on the road from the heavy rain.
26. The wash is hanging on the line and will soon dry.
27. The laundry will wash the clothes and deliver them.
28. You should wash your hands before coming to lunch.

29. The wind is whistling around the house.
30. The high wind blew a tree across the road.
31. The wind seems to come from every direction at once.
32. This wind is fast becoming a gale.

33. The house is very warm for this mild weather.
34. The family gave me a heart-warming welcome home.
35. This warm weather will be good for the garden.
36. We are going to have warmed-over food for supper.

37. I don't believe a word of the story you heard.
38. My friend's word is as good as his bond any day.
39. We have just had word that the family is well.
40. You took the words out of my mouth just then.

41. Someone must watch the camp fire tonight.
42. My wrist watch seems to be losing time.
43. Watch your step on the slippery sidewalk.
44. Who will watch the children on the playground?

45. The river at this point is too wide to swim across.
46. The question asked of the speaker was wide of the mark.
47. The news of the discovery was spread far and wide.
48. The highway is four lanes wide and as straight as a die.

49. It is time for the patient's morning walk.
50. The stores on the boardwalk are fascinating.
51. Someone sweeps the sidewalk every morning.
52. The teacher made the children walk a chalk line.

53. The woodpile is fast disappearing.
54. Someone should chop wood for the kitchen stove.
55. The foundations of the old house are made of wood.
56. There are five acres of woodland on the place.

57. There is a wading pool for the children on the playground.
58. I shall have to wade through the work as best I can.
59. We had to wade ashore from the boat as the tide was out.

60. We had to wade through deep snow to get to the highway.

35.   *Homophenous Words*

Wade, wait, wane, weight

We had to wade across the stream.

I had to wade through all the facts.

We had to wait an hour for the train.

You should wait for the rest of the party.

The moon is now on the wane.

That man's popularity will soon wane.

What is the weight of the package?

The butcher sometimes gives short weight.

Wad, wan, wand, want

He has a wad of money in his pocket.

The clothes were in a wad on the floor.

You look very wan since your illness.

Did you notice how wan the baby looks?

The children gave a wand drill at school.

I wish I could wave a magic wand over you.

What do you want me to do this afternoon?

That is what I thought you would want me to do.

Wide, wind, wine, whine, white

The river is wide at this point.

We like the wide open spaces of the desert.

How often do you wind your watch?

How long will it take you to wind up your business?

What kind of wine do you want?

Which wine glass shall I use?

The dog will whine to come into the house.

No one likes to hear a person whine.

The clothes are white from the hot sun.

Have you been through the White House?

36.   *Idiomatic Expressions and Adages*

Ways   We must find ways and means to carry on the
               work.

Wish   Why did you wish that work on me?

While   You should strike while the iron is hot.

White   Who has charge of the white elephant table?

Whole   The story was made out of the whole cloth.

Wipe   Wipe the slate clean and begin again.

Well   It is all well and good to talk that way.

Whim   We can't satisfy every whim and fancy.

Wild   We had a wild and woolly time on our trip.

Weather   You should keep a weather eye out for trouble.

LESSON VII

Short ĭ—Relaxed-Narrow

37. For the sound of short *i*, as in "pit," the lips have the natural
or relaxed movement, and the opening between the lips is
narrow.

38.   *Movement Words*

peat pit—heap hip

feat fit—eve if

wheat wit

39.   *Practice Words*

bill	ship	fish
film	thick	miss
will	live	rich
rim	dip	mint
sift	slip	list

40.   *Sentences*

1. There seems to be a mistake in the telephone bill.
2. Where can I get a twenty-dollar bill changed?
3. There is a large billboard beside the highway.
4. A pair of doves bill and coo outside my window.

5. Where can I buy more film for my camera?
6. The film was ruined by being over-exposed.
7. I put the film in the camera the wrong way.
8. There is a film of oil on the water from the boat.

9. Will you please drive for awhile?
10. The child's strong will makes him hard to control.
11. He willed himself to keep on to the end.
12. The father has willed everything to his family.

13. There is a rim of silver around the cup.
14. The rim of the new tumblers will not chip.
15. The tires on the old car are worn down to the rim.
16. Rimless glasses are more becoming to some people.

17. How many times should I sift the flour?
18. The workmen have to sift sand to make concrete.
19. We shall have to sift all the facts of the story.
20. The dust sifts in through the cracks around the window.

21. The merchant failed to ship our order on time.
22. The ship is ready to leave the pier when the tide changes.
23. The fruit will not spoil if shipped by airplane.
24. We were glad to get off the ship after the rough voyage.

25. The ice in the river is not thick enough for skating.
26. The cream is not thick enough to whip well.

27. The friends seem to be as thick as thieves.
28. The fog was so thick we had to drive slowly all the way.

29. We live in a small house in the country in the summer.
30. Will the flowers live in the house all winter?
31. We have to live up to our reputation.
32. We live near the best school in the town.

33. You will have to dip the pen in the ink.
34. Dip your hands in the water to cool them off.
35. We had to dip the water out of the boat.
36. We had to dip the water up in our hands for a drink.

37. We tried to slip by the guard at the door.
38. I wrote my name on a slip of paper and left it.
39. You can slip the note under my door if I am out.
40. That was just an unfortunate slip of the tongue.

41. Are you fishing for a compliment from me?
42. What kind of fish would you like for dinner?
43. Did you ever fish for brook trout in the mountains?
44. We went deep-sea fishing every day at the Shore.

45. If you miss the train you must wait an hour.
46. We miss the comforts of home when we are in camp.
47. Did you miss anything from the room when you came in?
48. You shouldn't miss the opportunity to go South.

49. Every member of the family is very rich.
50. The food at the restaurant was too rich for me.
51. We are rich in having so many wonderful friends.
52. The rich tones of the music were beautiful.

53. Do you like mint leaves in your iced tea?
54. Have you ever visited the United States Mint?
55. We grow mint and other herbs in our garden.
56. The men made a mint of money on their venture.

57. I have lost my shopping list and can't remember it.
58. Will you list the people as they come into the room?
59. How many men are on the waiting list for the job?
60. The boat had a bad list to the right after the accident.

41.   *Homophenous Words*

Bill, mill, pill

     It is time to pay the telephone bill.

     When do you think the bill will pass the Senate?

     There is a large flour mill in our town.

     The workers leave the mill when the whistle blows.

     That was a bitter pill for me to swallow.

     You should take one pill each day after lunch.

Limb, limp, lip

     A limb of the tree was broken off in the storm.

     Which limb of the tree shall I prune first?

     I am limp from the hot weather and humidity.

     The uncomfortable shoes made me limp home.

     Some people give lip service only to the church.

     What kind of lipstick do you like to use?

Dim, dip, nib, nip, tip

     The light in the room is too dim for me.

     Why do you take such a dim view of the future?

     I had only time enough to dip into the book.

     We had a dip in the ocean before breakfast.

     The nib of the pen was bent when it fell.

     The pen should have a new nib before it is used.

Unless protected the frost may nip the plants.

It was nip and tuck between the two boys in the race.

How large a tip should I leave for the waiter?

Be careful not to tip over the glass of water.

42.   *Idiomatic Expressions and Adages*

Give	Children should learn the give and take of play.
Bill	The book will fill the bill.
Pick	I have a bone to pick with you.
Sink	You are on your own and will have to sink or swim.
Fits	I have been able to work only by fits and starts.
Nip	We must nip the plan in the bud.
Lick	Someone will have to lick the report into shape.
Missed	The committee seems to have "missed the boat."
Mince	You don't have to mince matters with me.
Bib	I shall wear my best bib and tucker.

LESSON VIII

Short ŭ—Relaxed-Medium

43. For the sound of short *u,* as in "but," the lips are relaxed, and the opening between the lips is neither narrow nor wide, but is medium.

44.   *Movement Words*

bit but—hip hup

fin fun—if huff

win won

bet but—ebb hub

fen fun—eff huff

45.   *Practice Words*

bump	trust	tough
fun	punch	drum
sum	brush	crust
lump	dull	lunch
rough	thumb	touch

46.   *Sentences*

1. Be careful not to bump the car ahead of you.
2. I was surprised to bump into you when downtown.
3. Don't bump your head on that low shelf.
4. Where did you get the bump on your forehead?

5. We had fun on the picnic in the Park.
6. The remark was made in a spirit of fun.
7. Everyone should have some fun in life.
8. Please don't think we were making fun of you.

9. Do you carry a large sum of money with you?
10. What is the sum-total of the expenses?
11. To get home again is the sum of happiness.
12. Will you sum up the speaker's remarks?

13. The horse expects a lump of sugar when he sees me.
14. What can you model from a lump of clay?
15. We lumped all the expenses of the trip together.
16. The lump on my head was as big as a golf ball.

17. The ocean is very rough today and the waves are high.
18. Someone will get hurt if your play is so rough.
19. We had to rough it on the mountain climb.
20. We need a rough-and-ready fellow for the job.

21. Will you trust me to write the report?
22. We get a small income from the trust fund.
23. The trust company will lend you money on the house.
24. Put your trust in God and go ahead!

25. We served punch at the reception.
26. The speech was dull and lacked punch.
27. You will have to punch holes in the paper.
28. Did you see the Punch and Judy show at school?

29. There is a bad brush fire in the woods.
30. Someone just brushed past me in the dark.
31. Will you brush the crumbs off the table?
32. I saw the rabbit run into the underbrush.

33. The book is too dull and uninteresting to finish.
34. I had a dull time at the birthday party.
35. The carving knife is too dull to use without sharpening.
36. It is said that all work and no play makes Jack a dull boy.

37. The thumb of my glove needs to be mended.
38. The children like to play Thumbs Up.
39. The children should not thumb the pages of the book.
40. My fingers are so cold they are all thumbs.

41. The meat is too tough to cut with this knife.
42. We have a tough job on our hands to do this week.
43. Watch that man closely for he is a tough customer.
44. We had a tough time on the trip through the mountains.

45. I like to hear a school fife and drum corps.
46. Please don't drum on the table with your fingers.
47. It is fascinating to watch a good drummer.
48. We must drum up trade for the church bazaar.

49. There is a hard crust on the snow since the freeze.
50. The crust on the apple pie is brown and flaky.
51. You should throw the crusts of bread to the birds.
52. Some people have a crust and are a nuisance.

53. We like to have our lunch at twelve o'clock.
54. We ate lunch at a counter in the drug store.
55. I went out for a quick lunch as I was so busy.
56. Where do you suggest we have lunch today?

57. We have been out of touch with the family lately.
58. Who made the last touchdown in the game?
59. Do you use the touch system on the typewriter?
60. The new minister seems to have the common touch.

47.   *Homophenous Words*

Cub, come, cup, gum

    We saw a bear cub with its mother at the zoo.
    He is only a cub reporter for the afternoon paper.
    Be sure to come home early for the children's party.
    How did you come by that lovely new car?
    My cup of happiness is full and running over.
    There is always a paper cup by the water cooler.
    Do you chew gum for a dry mouth when driving?
    The gum drops are freshly made and easy to chew.

Dumb, dump, numb, tub

    I was so frightened I was too dumb to speak.
    There is a dumb waiter from the basement to the kitchen.
    There is a rubbish dump in the vacant lot.
    You may dump the groceries on the floor.
    My mind was numb from the shock of the news.
    The cold made my feet too numb to walk.
    The boat is just an old tub with a bad leak.

The laundry tub and washing machine are in the basement.

Bum, bump, mum, pump, pub

We had to bum around all morning between trains.

That was a bum job the workman did for us.

The bump in the road almost broke the springs of the car.

I wish I had as good a bump of location as you have.

You must keep mum about what I just told you.

We saw a beautiful "mum" at the flower show.

The pump in the kitchen is out of order.

It won't do any good to pump me for information.

The men spend every Saturday evening in the Pub.

You will find a pub in every village.

48.   *Idiomatic Expressions and Adages*

Up   Don't throw up the sponge just yet.

Must   You must be sure to get your beauty sleep.

Cut   That doesn't cut any ice with me!

Runs   It runs in the family to be tall.

Touch   A friend tried to touch me for five dollars.

Guns   You should stick to your guns.

Funny   The story struck my funny bone.

Young   The young man seems to be feeling his oats.

Hunted   We hunted here, there, and everywhere for the
          papers.

Null   The contract was null and void.

Lesson IX

Ah—Relaxed-Wide

49. For the sound of *ah,* as in "cart," the lips are relaxed and
the opening between the lips is the widest of the relaxed vowels.

50.   *Movement Words*

bid bud bard—hip hup harp
fin fun far—give cuff carve
bad bard—ham harm
fat far—have carve

51.   *Practice Words*

part	large	guard
far	harsh	alarm
mark	marble	calm
sharp	charge	march
palm	smart	starch

52.   *Sentences*

1. We found part of the motor missing.
2. We will go part of the way with you.
3. Which part of the chicken do you like?
4. The part-time work will pay you well.

5. It is too far to walk home from the station.
6. How far do you think you can make the money go?
7. The table is at the far end of the room.
8. How far away can you see to read the sign?

9. I hope you don't think I am an easy mark.
10. Someone will have to mark the examination papers.
11. We had to mark time for five minutes in the parade.
12. Be sure to mark the place in the book before closing it.

13. The knife is not sharp enough to cut butter!
14. You must keep a sharp lookout for the side road.
15. There is a sharp wind blowing from the north.
16. That man will drive a sharp bargain if not watched.

17. Do you know anyone who will read my palm?
18. The drive along the ocean is lined with palm trees.
19. The boys have just learned to palm a coin.
20. You needn't try to palm that old story off on me.

21. Where can I find a house for a large family?
22. The shoes are too large for me and rubbed my heel.
23. The hospital is a large place and well equipped.
24. The men who robbed the bank are still at large.

25. You should not be too harsh with the children.
26. The harsh voice of the speaker was very unpleasant.
27. The dress material has a harsh finish and will be durable.
28. The winds of March are usually harsh and disagreeable.

29. When spring comes the boys like to play marbles.
30. The Jefferson Memorial is made of white marble.
31. The old-fashioned table has a marble top.
32. The marble steps are badly worn and dangerous.

33. Please charge all my purchases to my account.
34. Don't let the salesman charge you too much.
35. Who has charge of the church supper next week?
36. You have been put in charge of the office force.

37. My eyes smart from the smoking chimney.
38. It is smart to save money for a rainy day.
39. Members of the Smart Set will be on hand.
40. The uniform gave the soldier a smart appearance.

41. Someone will have to stand guard tonight.
42. You should wear a guard over the diamond ring.
43. I will guard the papers for you with my life.
44. The football team broke through the opposing guard.

45. The police broadcast an alarm for the lost child.
46. Someone set off the burglar alarm in the bank.
47. I hope the news of the accident did not alarm you.
48. I forgot to set the alarm clock and overslept.

49. This must be the calm before the storm.
50. The river is calm this morning and as smooth as glass.
51. The speaker's calm manner made him easy to listen to.
52. Try to keep calm, the trouble is almost over.

53. Will you march in the Fourth of July parade?
54. I like to hear a brass band play a march.
55. The men were tired after a long day's march.
56. The March winds are often raw and disagreeable.

57. A starched collar is uncomfortable in hot weather.
58. The hot weather takes all the starch out of me.
59. We had cornstarch pudding with fruit sauce for supper.
60. The laundress should put more starch in the dress.

53.   *Homophenous Words*

Bar, mar, par

    I have a bar of chocolate in my pocket.
    There is an iron bar over the basement window.
    Water will not mar the varnish on the table top.
    Rain will not mar the pleasure of our trip.
    The stocks were sold at par on the open market.
    The boy's health has been below par for sometime.

Card, cart, guard

    I haven't yet played my trump card.
    Did you receive a card to the wedding reception?
    You are putting the cart before the horse.

Someone will have to cart off the rubbish.

I tried to put you on your guard before it happened.

Someone will have to guard the supplies at camp.

Art, hard, hart, heart

Have you been to the Art Museum lately?

He has the art of making friends easily.

What can we use to soften the hard water?

The work was hard but so interesting we enjoyed it.

We saw a hart at the edge of the river.

A hart ran into the woods as we passed by.

He has a soft heart for children and they like him.

He puts his heart and soul into everything he does.

54. *Idiomatic Expressions and Adages*

March	So you want to steal a march on your family.
Heart	Absence makes the heart grow fonder.
Ark	The dress looks as if it came out of the Ark.
Barn	We had to go around Robin Hood's barn to get home.
Hard	It was hard to keep body and soul together.
Lark	We got up with the lark this morning.
Card	I have one more card up my sleeve.
Stark	Those are the stark facts of the case.
Partial	We are partial to our own flesh and blood.
Barking	You are barking up the wrong tree.

LESSON X

R—Puckered Corners

55. For *r,* as in "reef," before a vowel, the lips show a drawing together or puckering at the corners. After a vowel, as in "arm," *r* tends to be slurred and often will show no movement.

56. *Movement Words*

feed weed reed
fed wed red
fag wag rag
fin win rid
fun won run
far what rah

57. *Practice Words*

read	raft	ripe
rest	room	raise
rich	rush	road
rough	rock	rain
raw	rope	rust

58. *Sentences*

1. It helps some people to relax to read in bed.
2. Which newspaper do you like to read each day?
3. I should be able to read the book in a few hours.
4. It is possible to read some people like a book.

5. We stopped at the hotel to rest for an hour.
6. The time has come for you to rest on your laurels.
7. I should like to meet the rest of your family.
8. You can rest assured everything is going to be all right.

9. The plants should have shade and a rich soil.
10. You will find the work will never make you rich.
11. The vegetables are rich in vitamins if properly cooked.
12. I had to tell the story as it was too rich to keep.

13. The road up the mountain was steep and rough.
14. We had a rough voyage home from overseas.

15. The boys are too rough in their play with the children.
16. The cold weather makes my hands rough and unsightly.

17. Everyone should eat some raw vegetables every day.
18. The roast beef is very tender and almost raw.
19. There is a cold raw wind blowing from the east.
20. The factory can't get raw materials for its work.

21. The boys like to swim out to the raft.
22. The men spent three days on a life raft.
23. The boys floated down the river on a raft.
24. There was a raft of people at the party.

25. There is always room for one more.
26. The room is too small for the crowd.
27. Where can I find a room with bath to rent?
28. There is plenty of room in the car for everyone.

29. Why are you in such a rush to get home?
30. We were caught in the late afternoon rush.
31. You must rush if you want to catch the train.
32. Some people are always in a rush but never do anything!

33. Be careful not to rock the boat in deep water.
34. There was a big rock in the middle of the road.
35. We found an unusual kind of rock in the field.
36. We could feel the house rock in the wind.

37. The police used a rope to keep the crowd back.
38. The cowboys will rope the cattle at the roundup.
39. You should not swim in the surf beyond the ropes.
40. The sidewalk was roped off for blocks after the fire.

41. The fruit was picked before it was ripe.
42. The children seem to be ripe for mischief.
43. The strawberries should be ripe in another week.
44. Oranges are said to be ripe before they are yellow.

45. We were told the rent is soon to be raised.
46. We shall have to raise more funds for the club.
47. What vegetables do you raise in your garden?
48. The children almost raised the roof in their play.

49. The road along the ocean is lined with palm trees.
50. The roadbed is very uneven since the bad weather.
51. I like to drive over a country road late in the day.
52. You should turn left at the fork of the road.

53. Do you think it is going to rain very hard?
54. How true it is that it never rains but it pours.
55. We were caught in a heavy downpour of rain going home.
56. There hasn't been any rain here for many months.

57. It is always better to wear out than rust out.
58. The hinges on the door are stiff with rust.
59. The knives will rust in this damp weather.
60. There is rust on the leaves of the plant.

59.   *Homophenous Words*

Roam, robe, rope

     I like to roam through the woods in the fall.
     We will roam over the country on our vacation.
     The robe is made of pure wool and is very warm.
     There is a laprobe in the car for cold days.
     We watched the cowboys rope the cattle at the Rodeo.
     The box was very carefully tied up with rope.

Root, route, rude

    The plants have not taken root.

    We must get to the root of the trouble.

    You should go by the shortest route.

    Which route will you take going home?

    The children were rude to their teacher.

    We spent the night in a rude shelter.

Read, red, rend, rent, wren

    Have you read the latest novel?

    I read the contract before signing it.

    The red necktie is very becoming.

    The sun was very red this morning.

    We saw the lightning rend the rock in two.

    The steam fitters rend the air with their noise.

    The rent is more than we can afford.

    Will you rent or buy the house?

    The wren built a nest in the bird house.

    The same wren comes back each year.

60. *Idiomatic Expressions and Adages*

Rule	There is no hard and fast rule to follow.
Rains	It never rains but it pours.
Roads	All roads do not lead to Rome.
Roses	Life is not always a bed of roses!
Rustle	Speak of angels and you will hear the rustle of their wings.
Wrong	The committee is working on the wrong tack.
Read	They are trying to read him out of the party.
Earth	We moved heaven and earth to get the information.
Railroad	Stop, look, and listen at the railroad crossing.
Reason	It stands to reason the plan is not workable.

Lesson XI

S, z, c (soft)—Extended-Narrow

61. For *s,* as in "saw," *z,* as in "zone," and *c,* as in "peace," the teeth are very close together, closer than for any other sound; the lips are extended and the opening is narrow.

62.

Movement Words

weed read seed
wed red said
wag rag sag
win rid sin
won run son
what rah sard

63.

Practice Words

seem	soup	piece
sent	saw	sour
sand	same	pace
sift	mice	race
sun	soap	wrist

64.

Sentences

1. The house seems to be in perfect order.
2. Things are not always what they seem.
3. You seem to be dreaming about something.
4. The roads seem to be cleared of snow.

5. The children were sent out to play.
6. We sent to the mail-order house for supplies.
7. The Post Office sent the package back for a better address.
8. I sent a messenger to the office with the money.

9. The wind blew the sand into my eyes and blinded me.
10. Someone will have to sand the road before it is safe.
11. The children like to play in the sand at the beach.
12. We had a sand storm while crossing the desert.

13. The snow sifts in under the front door.
14. You must sift the flour several times for the cake.
15. The workmen will sift the gravel for the builders.
16. We must sift the true from the false in the story.

17. The sun has been shining all day for a change.
18. What time does the sun rise in the morning?
19. Be careful not to get a sunburn when out sailing.
20. The sun was red when it came up this morning.

21. What kind of soup would you like for lunch?
22. The French keep the soup pot always on the stove.
23. Ask the butcher for a good soup bone with the meat.
24. Would you like a clear soup for the first course?

25. I saw you on the street one day last week.
26. We saw a movie last night at the neighborhood theater.
27. Which saw shall I use to cut the board in two?
28. You will get hurt if you monkey with the buzz saw!

29. That is the same old story you always tell.
30. Do you live in the same neighborhood as before?
31. The boys in the club are all about the same age.
32. I am tired of doing the same thing every day.

33. Someone should set a trap for the mice
34. The cat will catch the mice in the cellar.
35. The children were as quiet as mice at the movie.
36. How many mice were caught in the traps last night?

37. Wash your hands carefully with soap and water.
38. The soap flakes are very mild and good for dishwashing.
39. This soap is supposed to soften the hard water.
40. Don't let the soapsuds get into your eyes.

41. May I have a piece of bread and butter with the dessert?
42. The transaction was a bad piece of business for me.
43. Will you play a piece on the piano for our guests?
44. How many pieces should there be in the set of dishes?

45. The oranges are too sour for the baby.
46. The milk will sour if left out of the refrigerator.
47. The soil will sour in this hot, damp weather.
48. People with a sour disposition are never popular.

49. Your pace is so fast I can't keep up with you.
50. Why do you pace up and down the room at night?
51. I like to ride a horse that has an easy pace.
52. Someone should pace off the tennis court so we can play.

53. Did you ever see a horse race at Churchill Downs?
54. The boys raced home from school to play baseball.
55. There is a mill race down by the old mill.
56. It is bad for your car to race the motor so much.

57. The wristband on my watch is worn out.
58. A musician must have a flexible wrist.
59. The broken wrist has healed without trouble.
60. The workman's wrist is stiff with rheumatism.

65.   *Homophenous Words*

Sad, sand, sat

    Why did you look so sad when I came in?

We had a sad visit home last summer.

Do you like to play in the sand on the beach?

The children are playing in the sandbox.

We sat in the front row of the orchestra at the play.

How many people sat down to the table at Thanksgiving?

Sick, sing, sink

The food is so rich it will make you sick.

I am sick and tired of doing this work alone.

Will you sing for our friends after dinner?

The family likes to sing old songs together.

The sink is full of soiled dishes from the party.

The meaning of the talk has begun to sink in.

Sack, sag, sang, sank

We bought a sack of potatoes from the farmer.

The men all wore sack suits at the affair.

The foundations of the house have begun to sag.

The clothesline will sag if left too loose.

Who sang the solo in church this morning?

The campers sang and danced around the camp fire.

My heart sank when I saw the headlines in the paper.

The workmen sank the well one hundred feet.

66.   *Idiomatic Expressions and Adages*

Easy	That should be as easy as rolling off a log.
Once	That doesn't happen once in a blue moon.
Some	The new employee thinks he is some pumpkins.
Cents	I felt like thirty cents when I made the mistake.
Zeal	Zeal without knowledge is a dangerous thing.
Same	We are all in the same boat.
Side	You must have got out of the wrong side of the bed.
Swallow	That was a bitter pill to swallow.
Seed	The place has been allowed to go to seed.

Lesson XII

Sh, zh, ch, j and soft g—Lips-Projected

67. For *sh,* as in "sham," *zh,* as in azure (the *z* has the sound of *zh*), *ch,* as in "chap," *j,* as in "jam," and soft *g,* as in "gem," the lips are thrust forward or projected.

68.

Movement Words

reed seat sheet—ease each
red said shed—ess edge
rag sag shag—has hash

69.

Practice Words

sheet	shop	rush
shed	push	patch
jam	page	church
chip	shine	show
jump	catch	change

70.

Sentences

1. You must put clean sheets on the bed this morning.
2. It is easy to iron the sheets on a mangle.
3. It will be all right to use a sheet for a movie screen.
4. There are about five hundred sheets in a ream of paper.

5. My new overcoat sheds the water like a raincoat.
6. Can you shed any light on the question being discussed?
7. There is plenty of firewood in the woodshed.
8. The mountains form a watershed for the country.

9. There was a bad traffic jam on the road.
10. I can't jam anything more into the box.

11. The bus was jammed to the door with passengers.
12. What kind of jam would you like with your toast?

13. The new set of dishes chips very easily.
14. Will you chip in for the birthday present?
15. The boy is a chip off the old block.
16. You should have some chips to build the fire.

17. The loud noise made me almost jump out of the chair.
18. The stock market took a sudden jump today.
19. The horse fell when he refused to take the jump.
20. We manage to keep just one jump ahead of the others.

21. The best shops in town are on Main Street.
22. We must shop early for our Christmas presents.
23. Which specialty shop is the best for leather goods?
24. Do you like to window shop as you stroll along?

25. Don't push when you are getting on a bus.
26. Push the button to turn on the light in the room.
27. The police pushed the crowd back on the sidewalk.
28. We had to push the car around the corner when it stalled.

29. The message was brought to me by a page.
30. What is the number of the page you are reading?
31. We paged you at the hotel and couldn't find you.
32. Several pages are torn out of the telephone book.

33. The flowers should have more sunshine to thrive.
34. Where can I find someone to shine my shoes?
35. The children seemed to take a shine to you.
36. The sun shines in every room in the house.

37. There is just time to catch the train.
38. How many fish did you catch from the pier?
39. I hoped I would catch you at home this time.
40. Don't let me catch you doing that again.

41. We had to rush all day to get ready for the trip.
42. The crowd rushed forward to see the President.
43. We gathered rushes growing in the marsh.
44. Rushes are used to make baskets and chair-seats.

45. We'll have to patch up the old farmhouse.
46. We have a small vegetable patch in the back yard.
47. There is just a patch of blue sky to be seen.
48. Someone will have to patch the roof before it rains.

49. Which church in town has the largest congregation?
50. The church service was so long I went to sleep.
51. You are in the right church but the wrong pew.
52. Church notices are published in the Saturday papers.

53. We are going to the early show tonight.
54. Will you show me how you want the work done?
55. I like to look in the show windows along the Avenue.
56. The buds on the trees are beginning to show.

57. How much change do you have in your purse?
58. There is going to be a change in the weather.
59. What made you change your mind so suddenly?
60. You should have change for your bus fare before entering.

71.   *Homophenous Words*

Chain, jade, shade
      We have a chain on the front door.
      Do you like a chain stitch sewing machine?

The jade is a beautiful shade of green.

I saw the collection of jade at the museum.

You should draw down the shade.

The tree will shade you from the sun.

Chap, jam, jamb, sham

Do your hands chap in cold weather?

Your friend seems to be a fine chap.

We got into a bad traffic jam coming home.

The strawberry jam is perfect this year.

The door jamb is badly warped.

The window jamb should be nailed down.

I am afraid the man is a sham.

We watched a sham battle at camp.

Chewed, chute, June, jute, shoot

The puppy chewed my bedroom slippers.

The children chewed bubble gum in camp.

You can put the letter in the mail chute.

There is a linen chute in the hall.

June is the month of roses.

We leave for the country early in June.

Burlap bags are made from jute.

Jute is sometimes made into wrapping paper.

The farmer will have to shoot the rabbits.

Do you have a permit to shoot deer this fall?

72.   *Idiomatic Expressions and Adages*

Ship	Are you waiting for your ship to come in?
Shadow	Some people are afraid of their own shadow.
Church	I feel as poor as a church mouse!
Shouting	It is all over but the shouting.
Job	Why did you lie down on the job?
Pleasure	Business should come before pleasure.
Worship	Some people worship the almighty dollar.

Ashes	I repented in sackcloth and ashes for my mistake.
Push	He would do better if he had more push.
Dutch	It beats the Dutch the way children ask questions.

LESSON XIII

Long o͞o—Puckered-Narrow

73. For the sound of long *oo,* as in "cool," the lips are drawn together or puckered, and the opening between the lips is very narrow.

74.   *Movement Words*

beet bit boot—heap hip whom
feet fit food—eve if hoof
wheat wit wooed
read rid rude
seen sin soon—ease is ooze
cheat chin chew—teach dish

75.   *Practice Words*

pool	lose	juice
fool	move	food
rule	room	boost
boom	rude	roof
loom	moon	soon

76.   *Sentences*

1. Would you like to play a game of pool?
2. We must pool our resources to get capital.
3. Shall we swim in the pool or in the ocean?
4. The pool table is in the recreation room.

5. Don't let the big promises fool you.
6. Be careful for the machine is not foolproof.
7. I have been fooling around in the house all day.
8. The world is full of people who are easily fooled.

9. You should obey the traffic rules at all times.
10. Do as you please for there are no rules here.
11. Does anyone here know the rules of the game?
12. You should rule the lines on the page.

13. The town is having a boom in real estate.
14. We could hear the boom of the waves on the beach.
15. The houses were built in boom days and are shabby.
16. We are not going to boom your friend for President.

17. The newspapers say better times loom ahead of us.
18. How many operate looms in the factory?
19. The whir of the looms can be heard far away.
20. The hand loom is too small for the pattern.

21. You will lose time if you get out and walk.
22. Watch your umbrella or you will lose it.
23. You should not lose your temper over small things.
24. If you lose your way, wait where you are.

25. When do you plan to move into the house?
26. I think you made the wrong move that time.
27. If you will move over I can sit beside you.
28. It is time to move the plants indoors for the winter.

29. Our new car is very roomy and comfortable.
30. There wasn't a hotel room in the city to be had.
31. Did you advertise in the paper for a furnished room?
32. There was a roomful of people when we arrived.

33. I had a rude interruption in my reading.
34. I am afraid he will have a rude awakening.
35. There is never an excuse for anyone being rude.
36. We spent the night in a rude shelter in the woods.

37. There will be a new moon tonight but it will be cloudy.
38. The moon in Florida often makes it as light as day.
39. You are always mooning over your work when I come in.
40. We must wait for the moon to come up before we start.

41. I want the oranges that have the most juice.
42. The invalid should have beef juice every day.
43. Pour off the juice from the fruit for the salad.
44. We used beet juice to dye Easter eggs for the children.

45. We had to take all our food with us to camp.
46. We have enough food on hand to feed an army!
47. Your questions have given me food for thought.
48. What kind of food shall we take for the picnic?

49. What you told me boosted my morale.
50. We had to boost the children over the fence.
51. Who is responsible for boosting prices of food?
52. The advertisement should boost sales at the store.

53. There is a bad leak in the porch roof.
54. The boys like to climb to the roof of the barn.
55. We could see the red tile roof through the trees.
56. When will the workmen get the roof on the house?

57. How soon can you be ready to go with me?
58. It will soon be time to go home for dinner.
59. It is too soon to know what the weather will be like.
60. Summer will soon be here and the flowers will bloom.

77. *Homophenous Words*

Loom, loop

Our troubles always loom very large to us.

The scarf was woven by hand on a loom.

We drove with friends to the Loop in Chicago.

We must find some loophole in the arrangement.

Chews, choose, juice, shoes

The puppy chews everything he can find.

The boy chews his pencil as he studies.

Which house on the block would you choose?

I would choose that suit if I were you.

What kind of fruit juice do you prefer?

Will you have a small or large glass of orange juice?

These shoes are not suitable for walking.

The shoes are perfectly comfortable and good looking.

Boon, boot, mood, moon, moot

This rain is a boon to the farmers.

A long vacation is a boon to a tired worker.

The boot came up to my hips.

One boot is larger than the other.

Are you in the mood for a game of bridge?

The chief is in a black mood today.

There will be a full moon tonight.

Do you ever wish on the new moon?

That is a moot question.

We must avoid moot subjects at the meeting.

78. *Idiomatic Expressions and Adages*

Loose   You can't play fast and loose with the committee.

Cool   I had to cool my heels in the waiting room.

Rule   You needn't think you can rule the roost!

Moon   It won't do any good to cry for the moon.

Blue	That man is true blue.
Goose	The trip was a wild goose chase.
Two	The friends are two of a kind.
Chew	Be careful not to bite off more than you can chew.
Soon	The family will soon be down and out.
Boots	My heart was in my boots.

Lesson XIV

Short o͝o—Puckered-Medium

79. For the sound of short *oo,* as in "good," the lips are puckered, and the opening between the lips is neither narrow nor wide, but is medium.

80. *Movement Words*

boot book
food foot
wooed wood
rude rook
bet but put
fen fun foot
wen won wood
reck rug rook

81. *Practice Words*

pull	shook	foot
book	look	put
full	bush	wolf
wood	wool	cook

82. *Sentences*

1. The horses cannot pull such a heavy load.
2. I pulled the children around the block on the sled.

3. The engine was not heavy enough to pull the train.
4. The wreckers will pull the old house down.

5. I could not find the book in the Library.
6. How long will it take you to read the book?
7. The police will book the criminal at the station house.
8. I'll have to take a leaf out of your book.

9. The refrigerator is full of food left from dinner.
10. We are going to have a full day in town tomorrow.
11. There is a house full of children at home.
12. Be sure the gas tank is full before we start.

13. Someone should put more wood on the living room fire.
14. The woods are beautiful in the spring and fall.
15. The wood in the panel has an unusually beautiful grain.
16. The walls of the playroom are paneled in wood.

17. The wind shook the apples from the trees.
18. I shook hands with everyone in the room.
19. You shook the table while I was writing.
20. The high wind shook the house to its foundations.

21. You should never look a gift horse in the mouth.
22. Look in on us sometime when you are in town.
23. I saw a look of surprise on your face when I spoke.
24. The garden looks unusually beautiful this spring.

25. Why do you beat around the bush with me?
26. A bird in the hand is worth two in the bush.
27. The rose bush has more blossoms than usual.
28. The rabbits were hiding under a bush in the garden.

29. The material is one hundred percent wool.
30. The house is too warm for a wool dress.
31. I haven't enough wool to finish the sweater.
32. There is steel wool on the kitchen shelf.

33. The soldiers were tired and footsore from the march.
34. You should go to the foot of the class for that.
35. We walked every foot of the way home from town.
36. You will have to put your foot down with the children.

37. Where did you put the magazine that has just come?
38. The children are coming and it's time to put dinner on.
39. The steamboat has just put out from the dock.
40. Will you put in a good word for me with the boss?

41. It is hard for them to keep the wolf from the door.
42. The boys in camp wolf their food unless watched.
43. That man is said to be the Wolf of Wall Street.
44. We are not worried as he has cried "wolf" too often.

45. Who is going to cook the dinner for the crowd?
46. I found the recipe in my mother's cook book.
47. Some men learned to cook while in the army.
48. People who enjoy food usually make good cooks.

83.   *Homophenous Words*

Bull, pull

    The bulldog guards the house when we are away.

    Have you ever seen a bullfight in Mexico?

    We had a candy-pull for the school children.

    Haven't you any political pull to help you get a job?

Could, good

    I am sure you could go with us if you wanted to.

    Do you think we could have driven faster over that road?

We have had a good day with our friends at the shore.
It was good to be home and to see old friends.
Wood, would
Where can we buy wood for the fireplace?
The wood is too green to burn well.
What would you like to do this afternoon?
This would be a perfect day for a picnic.

84.   *Idiomatic Expressions and Adages*

Foot   I could hardly put one foot before the other.
Woods   The invalid is not yet out of the woods.
Good   We are leaving town for good and all.
Look   Be sure to look before you leap.
Pull   I won't pull your chestnuts out of the fire.
Full   The party was in full swing when we arrived.
Hook   We will succeed by hook or by crook.
Books   I don't want to be in your black books.
Put   You put your foot in it that time.
Cooks   Too many cooks will spoil the broth.

LESSON XV

Aw, o in "Orb"—Puckered-Wide

85. For the sounds of *aw,* as in "cawed," and of the *o,* in "orb,"
the lips are slightly puckered, and the opening between the
lips is the widest of the puckered vowels.

86.   *Movement Words*

boot book pawn—whom orb
food foot fawn—hoof cough
wooed wood walk
rude rook raw
soon sook sought—booze puss pause
shoot shook short—push porch

87.   *Practice Words*

bought	short	ball
fall	dawn	wharf
walk	lawn	taught
raw	tall	sauce
saw	call	caught

88.   *Sentences*

1. We have bought a house in the country.
2. Have you bought the supplies for the week?
3. Someone has bought the house next door.
4. We almost bought out the store on our shopping trip.

5. The thermometer has begun to fall.
6. The waterfall was a beautiful sight.
7. The fall is the best season of the year.
8. You didn't fall for that line, did you?

9. I walk to work every morning in good weather.
10. The Park is only a short walk from here.
11. You must not ride the bicycle on the sidewalk.
12. He had to walk the horse because he was lame.

13. The weather in March is usually cold and raw.
14. It is unwise to drink raw milk under any circumstances.
15. A raw vegetable salad is full of vitamins.
16. The factory could not get enough raw materials.

17. I saw you painting the house as I went by.
18. We saw just the house we want for our family.
19. I hope you saw all your friends during vacation.
20. We have sawed enough firewood for the winter.

21. We spent a short time in the country.
22. That is the long and short of the matter.
23. Be careful not to let anyone short-change you.
24. I was short of time and couldn't wait for you.

25. We left the house before dawn for our long trip.
26. It just dawned on me what you meant by the remark.
27. Everything was very quiet when we got up at dawn.
28. That goes back to the dawn of civilization.

29. Our lawn is unusually green for this time of year.
30. The baby's dress is made of fine lawn.
31. We put our chairs on the lawn where it is cool.
32. What will make the grass grow on our shaded lawn?

33. How tall is the Empire State Building?
34. The boy is very tall for his age.
35. Which state grows the tallest corn?
36. Which is the tallest building in the world?

37. Can I call for you on the way home?
38. Have you read "The Call of the Wild"?
39. You can call me on the telephone at any time.
40. We made a short call on our new neighbors.

41. Are you going to the Big League ball game?
42. Are the boys playing ball in the back yard?
43. What can be done to keep the ball rolling?
44. The President tossed out the first ball of the season.

45. The boat is just coming up to the wharf.
46. We bought the fish down at the Fishing Wharf.
47. We went to the wharf to watch the boats come in.
48. The boat will soon unload its cargo at the wharf.

49. The children were taught to swim at camp.
50. I hope the experience has taught you a lesson.
51. When and where were you taught to drive a car?
52. Have you ever taught small children to read?

53. What kind of sauce do you like with fish?
54. Apple sauce was served with the baked ham.
55. The cream sauce on the cauliflower was just right.
56. The French are experts in making sauces of all kinds.

57. We caught the last train home from town.
58. I was caught off my guard when the question was asked
59. The children caught cold playing in the snow.
60. At last I have caught up with the load of work.

89.   *Homophenous Words*

Fawn, fought

    We saw a fawn beside the road as we passed.

    Some employers like their employees to fawn on them.

    We fought for a place to see the parade.

    The Union fought for an increase in wages.

All, awl, hall, haul

    The news is all over town by now.

    All the family are away in the country.

    The shoemaker uses an awl in his work.

    You should have an awl to make holes in the leather.

    Where is the Hall of Fame in New York?

    I will wait for you in the hall downstairs.

    The company will haul the freight in a truck.

    It is a long haul from Boston to Chicago.

Ball, bawl, mall, maul, pall

    There will be a ball game today at the Arena.

    Will you buy a ball of twine when you go downtown?

    We could hear the calf bawl for its mother.

Did the boss bawl you out for the mistake?
There was a band concert on the Mall.
We strolled around the Mall in the Park.
The men used a maul to drive in the stakes.
The children should not be allowed to maul the puppies.
That music will pall on me after awhile.
There is a heavy pall of smoke over the town today.

90.   *Idiomatic Expressions and Adages*

Fought	The explorers fought their way through the jungle.
Tall	It runs in our family to be very tall.
Fall	You will have to fall in line with the rest of us.
Salt	The new workman doesn't seem to be worth his salt.
Wall	The army fought with its back to the wall.
Calls	That man always calls a spade a spade.
Ball	We must keep the ball rolling.
Raw	The new recruits were given a raw deal.
Gall	It was like gall and wormwood to apologize.
Law	No one should take the law into his own hands.

LESSON XVI

Th—Tongue-to-Teeth

91. For *th,* as in "thin," and "then," the point of the tongue shows either between the teeth or just behind the upper teeth.

92.   *Movement Words*

see she thee—tease teach teeth
said shed then—ess edge eth
sad shad that—has hash hath
suck shuck thug—us hush doth
ars arch hearth
sort short thought

93. *Practice Words*

thief	thaw	south
thank	throw	third
thick	worth	bath
thought	fifth	wealth
thumb	north	thread

94. *Sentences*

1. The thief must have come in the second-story window.
2. The police caught the thief before he could get away.
3. The thief turned everything upside down in the house.
4. A thief stole our automobile while we were in the store.

5. Thank you for all your kindness to me when I was ill.
6. That is a thankless job you have given me to do.
7. Have you written all your thank-you letters?
8. You shouldn't expect any thanks for the work.

9. The fog is too thick to see to drive the car.
10. I'd like a thick juicy beefsteak for dinner.
11. The rug in the living room was thick under my feet.
12. The foundation of the house is a foot thick.

13. There isn't a thought on the subject in my head.
14. I thought you were going to help me with the work.
15. Be sure to give me a thought while you are away.
16. I never thought about the appointment until too late.

17. We had to twiddle our thumbs for an hour.
18. Some people seem to live by rule of thumb.
19. We turned thumbs down on the suggestion.
20. It is all right for the baby to suck his thumb.

21. We will plant the trees when the ground thaws.
22. I was so cold I thought I would never thaw out.
23. How long will it take to thaw the frozen pipes?
24. We must cut the ice in the river before it thaws.

25. I had to throw my clothes on in a hurry.
26. Throw your wet coat over the chair to dry.
27. You should throw out the old newspapers when read.
28. Don't let the horse throw you when it shies.

29. The dress isn't worth the money you paid for it.
30. The matter you brought up is worth thinking about.
31. We bought five dollars' worth of groceries for them.
32. The house is worth more than has been offered for it.

33. Our house is the fifth from the corner.
34. Fifth Avenue in New York is a famous street.
35. We are leaving for home on the fifth of November.
36. This is the fifth time I have tried to see you.

37. The north side of the house is cold in winter.
38. We spend our summers in a camp in the North Woods.
39. You should turn north when you come to the crossroads.
40. The family comes from north of the Mason-Dixon line.

41. You will get a better view from the south window.
42. We have had a cold winter in the South.
43. You will need some warm clothes in the South.
44. The prevailing winds in the summer are from the south.

45. We will be paid on the third of the month.
46. Our car is parked around the corner on Third Street.
47. That is the third largest department store in town.
48. Be sure to turn right at the third traffic light.

49. There is a bird bath in the garden.
50. You can rent a bathhouse on the beach.
51. The bath is just across the hall from my room.
52. It is time for the children's bath and a bedtime romp.

53. There is a great deal of wealth in this town.
54. It is true that wealth does not always bring happiness.
55. The United States is said to be the wealthiest nation.
56. There is a wealth of material to choose from.

57. Will you thread the sewing machine for me?
58. We had to thread our way through the traffic.
59. The thread on the screw is worn smooth.
60. Where will I find some white cotton thread?

95.   *Homophenous Words*

Thawed, thought
> The ice in the river has thawed very rapidly.
>
> We must wait until the ground is thawed out before planting.
>
> I thought this morning it was going to rain.
>
> The new president of the company is well thought of.

Thumb, thump
> The boys will thumb their way home.
>
> Some people are said to have a "green thumb."
>
> The box fell on the floor with a loud thump.
>
> I was so frightened I could hear my heart thump.

Thick, thing, think
> The soup was thick with vegetables.
>
> He lays the flattery on thick.
>
> We have put everything in the car for the trip.
>
> There isn't a thing to do for awhile.
>
> What do you think about the news?
>
> I must have time to think the matter over.

96. *Idiomatic Expressions and Adages*

Both   He always lands on both feet.
Things   It is hard to be all things to all men.
Length   We like to keep some people at arm's length.
Mouth   My heart was in my mouth on the mountain road.
Thirty   I felt like thirty cents when I got lost.
Thread   I lost the thread of the conversation.
Worth   The contract isn't worth the paper it is written on.
Fifth   I felt like the fifth wheel at the dinner.
Truth   Truth is often stranger than fiction.

Lesson XVII

L—Pointed Tongue-to-Teeth

97. For *l*, as in "leaf," the point of the tongue touches the upper gum. The movement is seen as the tongue leaves the gum.

98. *Movement Words*

she thee lee—teach teeth deal
shed then let—edge eth ell
shad that lad—hash hath Hal
chick thick lick—myth mill
shuck thug luck—hush doth hull
shard lard—harsh hearth Carl
shook look—push pull
short thought lord—north tall

99. *Practice Words*

leave	large	boil
left	look	bowl
lamp	lose	fell
lift	feel	while
lump	whole	trail

100. *Sentences*

1. We must leave on our trip early in the morning.
2. You may leave the work for me to do later.
3. I am taking a week's leave of absence.
4. You shouldn't leave the windows open when you go out.

5. We left the meeting before it was over.
6. A left-handed pitcher is called a southpaw.
7. Someone left the front door open when he came in.
8. We will have warmed leftovers for supper.

9. The street lamps were turned off early today.
10. The three-way lamp gives a better light.
11. Oil lamps are still used on many farms.
12. We should have one more lamp in the room.

13. The box is too heavy for you to lift alone.
14. The fog will probably lift in a few hours.
15. A friend gave me a lift in his car going to town.
16. You should have rubber lifts put on your shoes.

17. Do you want lump or granulated sugar for your coffee?
18. We will lump all the expenses for our trip South.
19. What is the lump sum due the house for food?
20. If you don't like what I say you can lump it!

21. There is a large elm tree in front of the house.
22. The men who robbed the bank are still at large.
23. The house is much too large for our small family.
24. We gave the store a large order for groceries.

25. You look unusually well in your new suit.
26. Be sure to look in on us when you come to town.

27. I must look into the question before answering.
28. We shall have to look over the property before buying.

29. Did you ever lose your way in the woods?
30. You will lose your purse if you are not careful.
31. If you don't run you will lose your train for home.
32. I don't want to lose my place in line at the cafeteria.

33. Do you feel tired after the long walk before breakfast?
34. We had to feel our way through the house in the dark.
35. I like to feel the breeze blowing on my face.
36. We feel for you in your trouble and want to help.

37. Shall we give the whole story to the newspapers?
38. We were busy with housecleaning the whole time you were away.
39. Do you want whole wheat bread or white for the sandwiches?
40. There is a wholesome atmosphere in the school room.

41. You will find the water in the boiler always hot.
42. Will you have boiled or baked potatoes for dinner?
43. The story of the man's treatment made my blood boil.
44. Be careful not to let the pot boil over on the stove.

45. Who has made the best bowling score for the club?
46. The news that has just come almost bowled me over.
47. There is always a bowl of fruit on the table.
48. We are going to the Rose Bowl for the football game.

49. I fell into the water from the wharf while fishing.
50. The children fell into line at the fire drill.
51. The thermometer fell twenty degrees this morning.
52. I made the seam of the cotton dress with a French fell.

53. What shall we do to while away the time?
54. You may use our apartment while we are away.
55. We haven't seen the family in a long while.
56. You might as well stay while you are here.

57. We followed the trail up the mountain.
58. We have been trailing you all over town.
59. Did you ever travel through the country in a trailer?
60. The roses trail over the fence beside the road.

101.   *Homophenous Words*

Lack, lag, lank

>   The company lack money for the deal.
>   There is no lack of work to be done.
>   The children always lag behind.
>   There is a two weeks' lag in payments.
>   The boy is lean and lank but strong and healthy.
>   The woodsman has a lean and lank figure.

Loam, lobe, lope

>   The plants require a rich loam in the soil.
>   The loam will make the plants grow rapidly.
>   The earring hurt the lobe of my ear.
>   The lobe of my ear was injured in the fall.
>   She let the horse lope when almost home.
>   A lope is an easy gait for a horse.

Lade, laid, lain, late

>   We had to lade the water out of the tub.
>   The men will lade the cargo on the vessel before it sails.
>   The hens have laid well this summer.
>   I laid the book on the table in the living room.
>   The children have lain down for a nap.
>   How long have the apples lain on the ground?
>   It is never too late to mend.
>   You will be late for school unless you hurry.

102.   *Idiomatic Expressions and Adages*

Louder   Actions speak louder than words.
Fuel   That will only add fuel to the fire.
Led   The children led us a merry chase.
Leaf   There was only time to leaf through the book.
Like   Like father, like son.
Wool   Don't let anyone pull the wool over your eyes.
Feel   All the kindness made me feel cheap.
Loaf   Half a loaf is better than no bread.
Line   We had to walk the chalk line.
Life   The Constitution offers us life, liberty, and the
          pursuit of happiness.

LESSON XVIII

T, d, n—Flat Tongue-to-Gum

103. For *t,* as in "tie," *d,* as in "die," and *n,* as in "nigh," the flat edge of the tongue touches the upper gum. The teeth are close together, which makes the tongue movement a difficult one to see; sometimes reliance must be had upon the context.

104.   *Movement Words*

thee lee tea—teeth deal deed
then let ten—eth ell Ed
that lad tan—hath Hal hat
thug luck tuck—doth hull hut

105.   *Practice Words*

team	dark	fine
debt	name	pet
tap	talk	town
tip	mold	deep
dump	fit	meet

106.   *Sentences*

1. The school has a strong football team this year.
2. We can finish on time if we team up for the work.
3. The farmer should have a team of horses for the work.
4. The baseball team spends the winters in Florida.

5. The debt on the house will soon be paid off.
6. The interest on the debt is paid quarterly.
7. I am indebted to you for the help you have given.
8. We should all be concerned about the national debt.

9. Someone tapped me on the shoulder as I passed.
10. The hot water tap is leaking and should be repaired.
11. We haven't begun to tap our natural resources.
12. We have plenty of material for the building on tap.

13. How large a tip shall I leave for the waiter?
14. Can you give me a tip on the stock market?
15. I tipped the scales at one hundred and twenty pounds.
16. It was so late we tiptoed through the house.

17. Why are you down in the dumps today?
18. This place is the worst dump I ever saw.
19. The boys like to play with their toy dump cart.
20. The Army has an ammunition dump a mile away.

21. It grows dark very early these days.
22. This room is too dark to read lips.
23. You should wear dark clothes for the trip.
24. We shall try to get home before dark.

25. What is the name of the town we just passed?
26. You are to name the day for our next meeting.

27. Some people are never given a nickname.
28. The baby has the same name as his father.

29. Who is going to talk at the meeting?
30. The baby is just learning to talk.
31. Some people like to hear themselves talk.
32. You talk so softly I cannot understand you.

33. We made the pudding in individual molds.
34. Everything molds in this damp weather.
35. There is mold on the jar of preserves.
36. Newspapers help to mold the opinions of the public.

37. Which man is best fitted for the job?
38. It was hard to fit the furniture into the room.
39. The shoes are a perfect fit and just what I want.
40. The suit isn't fit to wear until it has been pressed.

41. This is going to be a fine day for a picnic.
42. We were fined for parking in the wrong place.
43. The print on the contract was too fine to read.
44. The picture is a fine example of photography.

45. You shouldn't pet a strange dog.
46. Who is teacher's pet in the class?
47. Every child likes to have his own pet.
48. The small boy is the pet of the neighborhood.

49. If you are going to town this morning may I go too?
50. Some people have small-town minds and are gossips.
51. Everyone knows everyone else in this small town.
52. We are very soon going back to town for the winter.

53. The man has a very deep bass voice.
54. I was deep in thought when you spoke to me.
55. The book is too deep and dry to interest me.
56. It is easier to swim in deep water than in shallow.

57. The two roads meet two miles from the house.
58. We are to meet the rest of the party at three o'clock.
59. I should like to have you meet my family some time.
60. Are you going to the school track meet this afternoon?

107.   *Homophenous Words*

Knees, niece

> My knees are stiff from climbing the stairs.
> I scrubbed the floor on my hands and knees.
> Is your niece going to college this fall?
> Our niece paid us a long visit this summer.

Dame, name, nape, tame, tape

> Dame Witty was a clever actress.
> The speaker at the club was a Colonial Dame.
> Your name is very familiar as it is a family name.
> You will be allowed to name the new baby.
> She wears her hair in a bun at the nape of her neck.
> The barber shaved his hair at the nape of the neck.
> The bear cubs were tame enough for pets.
> The entertainment was so tame I was bored.
> Someone should be able to cut the red tape.
> Be sure to seal the package with Scotch tape.

Dear, deer, near, tear, tier

> Everyone in that family is dear to me.
> The furniture is too dear for my pocketbook.
> We saw many deer in the National Park.

The deer come to the house to be fed.

The house is too near the railroad.

We are going home this afternoon the near way.

The strong light from the window makes my eyes tear.

A tear dropped on the page as she wrote the letter.

Our seats at the ball game are in the third tier.

You will find the book in the first tier of shelves.

108.   *Idiomatic Expressions and Adages*

Act	Don't act like a dog in the manger.
Day	I walked on air all day I was so happy.
Late	It is better to be late than never to come at all.
Turn	The pancakes were done to a turn.
Attempt	We will do or die in the attempt.
Night	The students turned night into day.
Dandy	I am fine and dandy today.
Nose	You shouldn't poke your nose into other people's business.
News	The news came like a bolt from the blue.
Bite	Don't bite the hand that feeds you.

LESSON XIX

K, hard c, hard g, ng, nk—Throat-Movement

109. For *k,* as in "kin," hard *c,* as in "cat," hard *g,* as in "go," *ng,* as in "rang," and *nk,* as in "rank," the movement is very slight and if seen at all it will be a drawing up of the throat muscles just above the Adam's apple. Usually these sounds must be revealed by the context and if seen at all, must be seen while the eyes are on the mouth.

110.   *Practice Words**

keep	cut	walk
get	cool	leak
can	good	pick
give	call	long
card	cold	bank

111.   *Sentences*

1. Be sure to keep the children off the street.
2. Why do you keep the car to the middle of the road?
3. You may keep the book from the library for four weeks.
4. It is hard to keep track of all the changes being made.

5. We get our mail before leaving in the morning.
6. What am I to get out of the deal for myself?
7. I shall get home from the meeting as early as possible.
8. We shall have to get up early in the morning tomorrow.

9. The oil can is almost empty and should be filled.
10. I will open a can of mushroom soup for lunch.
11. We canned all the fruit and vegetables we could.
12. Can you help me move the furniture in the living room?

13. How much will you give me for the March of Dimes?
14. The other side has refused to give in an inch.
15. His entire life has been given in service to others.
16. We give away our old clothes while they are still good.

17. I'll leave one of my business cards for you.
18. What card game would you like to play?

* These words are very difficult; do not insist upon having them seen apart from the thought of a sentence. Be careful to say the words naturally and without exaggeration.

19. You will find all the names in the card file.
20. Did you receive a card for the wedding reception?

21. The grass should be cut every two weeks.
22. We tried to take a short cut home and got lost.
23. The knife is so dull it wouldn't cut butter!
24. Someone cut us off in the middle of the conversation.

25. The weather is cool enough for an open fire.
26. Why are you so cool toward me these days?
27. I like to take a walk in the cool of the evening.
28. We must stop long enough for the engine to cool off.

29. Is there a good movie downtown this week?
30. It is a good mile from the farm to the next house.
31. The young man comes of a very good family.
32. This sunshine will be good for the invalid.

33. Please call me at seven o'clock in the morning.
34. I hope no one calls on me for a speech at the banquet.
35. She is subject to call from the hospital day and night.
36. We are expecting a call from some friends any day.

37. Turn on the heat as this room is too cold.
38. We are going to have a cold supper Sunday night.
39. The lecture was uninteresting and left me cold.
40. Green is a cold color for a north room.

41. It is too far to walk home from town.
42. Someone should sweep the sidewalk this morning.
43. We have walked over this road many times before.
44. We had to walk the horse because he seemed to be lame.

45. I hope the news will not leak out for awhile.
46. It is hard to find the leak in a shingle roof.
47. The water has leaked out of the basin onto the floor.
48. Have the workmen found the leak in the gas pipe?

49. Why does everyone have to pick on me?
50. Please pick up the newspapers from the floor.
51. You may have your pick of the books on the shelf.
52. The workmen will have to use pick and shovel.

53. That is the long and short of the matter.
54. It is a long time since I have seen you.
55. The meeting was so long I was bored and sleepy.
56. The club has a long list of inactive members.

57. What time does the bank open in the morning?
58. Can we bank on you for help with the work?
59. We climbed up the steep bank of the river.
60. Someone should bank the fire for the night.

112. *Homophenous Words*

Beak, meek, peak, peek

The bird has a very long beak.

The eagle's beak is very strong.

It doesn't pay to be too meek.

That man only pretends to be meek.

I hope prices have reached their peak.

The view was beautiful from the mountain peak.

The baby loves to play peek-a-boo.

Peek in the window and see who is in the room.

Rack, rag, rang, rank, wrack

I had to rack my brains to find an answer.

Put the suitcase in the luggage rack overhead.

You should have a rag to wipe the windshield.

Rag paper will last for many years.

We rang the doorbell but no one was at home.

The fire alarm rang twice this morning.

Who has the highest rank in the company?

The butter was too rank to use.

Everything on the place is going to wrack and ruin.

Gild, gilt, guilt, killed, kiln, kilt

We shall have to gild the picture frame.

What do we mean by "Gild the lily"?

The gilt is worn off the frame of the painting.

Do you like the gilt on the ballroom chairs?

Do you believe in the guilt of the defendant?

The expression of his face showed his guilt.

The plan was killed in the committee meeting.

The chickens for market have been killed.

The pottery has not come out of the kiln.

There is a brick kiln in the outskirts of town.

The Scotsman wore his kilt in the parade.

The schoolgirl wore a blouse and kilt to school.

113.   *Idiomatic Expressions and Adages*

Give	You must give an account of yourself.
Cases	Don't forget that circumstances alter cases.
Gall	The new medicine the doctor gave me was as bitter as gall.
Glove	The politician is hand in glove with the new appointee.
Cuts	The argument cuts no ice with me!
Knock	The meeting was a knock down and drag out affair.
Cart	That is putting the cart before the horse.
Actions	Actions speak louder than words.

LESSON XX

Diphthong Ow

114. For *ow*, as in "how," the first movement is like that for *ah*, as in "ha," the relaxed-wide; but for *ow* this relaxed-wide movement is followed by a very evident puckered movement.

115.   *Contrast Words*

Notice the puckering of the lips for *ow* which *ah* does not have.

mouse—mars	doubt—dart
pout—part	cow—car
loud—lard	how—ha

116.   *Practice Words*

pound	shout	ground
found	loud	frown
wound	town	brown
round	south	plow
sound	mouth	crowd

117.   *Sentences*

1. We buy our vegetables by the pound at the market.
2. The waves pound on the beach after a storm.
3. The lost dog was taken to the City Pound.
4. You will have to pound the post into the ground.

5. We found all the family at home when we arrived.
6. If you found the money it should be reported.
7. We found our way home from the picnic without trouble.
8. We found out the truth of the matter too late.

9. I wound all the wool for the sweater into balls.
10. I wound the scarf around my neck as it was so cold.
11. The grandfather clock has not been wound for a week.
12. The river wound through the valley to the ocean.

13. We took a roundabout way home to see old friends.
14. The policeman must go on his rounds every night.
15. There are a round dozen oranges left in the box.
16. We gathered around the camp fire to tell stories.

17. There was not a sound in the house when I went in.
18. The boys sail their boat all day on the Sound.
19. All the apples in the barrel seem to be sound.
20. The business is sound and would seem a good investment.

21. You don't have to shout at me to make me hear.
22. The children like to shout when they are playing.
23. We gave a shout of joy when the good news came.
24. The captain had to shout his orders because of the wind.

25. The radio is too loud for me to enjoy it.
26. The colors of the suit are too loud for the occasion.
27. Am I speaking loud enough for you to hear me?
28. We heard a loud roar coming from the crowd in the street.

29. Do you prefer to live in a small town?
30. Our farm is five miles from the nearest town.
31. The town meeting lasted until eleven o'clock.
32. Our town will celebrate Old Home Week this summer.

33. The south side of town is the best section.
34. Are you going South for the winter months?
35. How long has your family lived in the South?
36. North or south, east or west, home is best.

37. We made a trip to the mouth of the river.
38. The man was too loud-mouthed to be acceptable.
39. Be careful not to mouth your words when speaking.
40. The smell of the food made my mouth water.

41. That man seems to have both feet on the ground.
42. The airplane was grounded and the trip canceled.
43. The ground is just right for putting in the seed.
44. The snow melts as soon as it touches the ground.

45. Some people frown upon everything that is new.
46. If you frown so much it will make wrinkles.
47. The strong sunlight made me frown in the picture.
48. Why did you frown when we came into the room?

49. The meat was browned to a turn in the roaster.
50. The leaves have turned brown from the dry weather.
51. The brown handbag matches my hat and shoes.
52. I was in a brown study when you interrupted me.

53. The snow plow will soon clear the road to town.
54. When will you plow the field for winter wheat?
55. We had to plow our way through the heavy snow.
56. Someone will have to plow the ground for a garden.

57. Don't get into a big crowd if you can help it.
58. There was a big crowd at the stadium for the ball game.
59. I am afraid I will crowd you if I get into the car.
60. Everyone tried to crowd into the bus at the same time.

118.   *Homophenous Words*

Bow, bough, mow

    We must bow our heads in reverence at the service.
    The opera singer had to take another bow.

The wind broke off a bough of the tree.

The bough of the apple tree is heavy with fruit.

The children like to play in the hay mow.

The hay was stored in the mow before it began to rain.

Crowd, crown, crowned, ground

There was a large crowd around the stage door.

We can't crowd another person into the car.

I hope success will crown your efforts.

We saw the British crown in the Tower of London.

Princess Juliana was crowned Queen of the Netherlands.

Who was crowned Queen of the May at college?

The ground is too wet to plant the garden.

Be careful not to ground the boat on the sandbar.

Bound, bout, mound, mount, pound, pout

We shall soon be bound for home.

Can you bound the state of Pennsylvania?

Are you going to the boxing bout?

She is just over a bout with the flu.

The house is built on a mound.

There were many relics in the Indian mound.

We must mount the pictures in the album.

Can you mount the horse from the ground?

We had to pound the posts into the ground.

Please get another pound of butter at the store.

The baby will pout if he cannot have what he wants.

No one likes to see a person pout.

119. *Idiomatic Expressions and Adages*

Account	You must give an account of yourself.
House	We worked all day like a house afire.
Shouting	It is all over but the shouting.
Around	How can you get around the new rules?
Spout	All our possessions have gone up the spout.

Growl	I heard the men growl about the heavy work.
Fowl	It is neither fish, flesh, nor fowl, nor good red herring.
Round	How much do we owe in round numbers?
Loud	No one likes a loud-mouthed person.
Mouth	You may soon be laughing out of the other side of your mouth!

Lesson XXI

Diphthong Long ō

120. For long *o,* as in "go," we have what may be described as a contracting puckered movement, beginning with a slight puckering and somewhat wide opening of the lips (like the puckered-wide for aw) and becoming more puckered.

121.   *Movement Words*

bough beau
vow foe
wow woe
rout rote
sound zone—house hose
shout shoat—couch coach
thou though—mouth both
loud load—howl hole
now no—out oat

122.   *Practice Words*

poll	roll	loaf
bore	sold	pour
force	shore	sole
vote	both	rose
wore	road	toast

123.   *Sentences*

1. You must be sure to go to the polls to vote.
2. Fortunately, we do not have a poll tax in this state.
3. Someone should poll the members of the club.
4. We have to vote at the nearest polling place.

5. His eyes seemed to bore through me.
6. Don't let me bore you with my story.
7. Who bore the brunt of the heavy work at the office?
8. A truck bore down on us as we crossed the street.

9. The plants have been forced in a hothouse.
10. Someone will have to force the door open.
11. I don't want to force you to go to the meeting.
12. How large a police force does the town have?

13. Those who do not vote in an election should be fined.
14. Everyone at the meeting voted it a failure.
15. How many votes were cast for President of the club?
16. Which amendment to the Constitution gave votes to women?

17. We wore our old clothes while at camp.
18. I am afraid I wore you out with the long discussion.
19. The argument wore my patience to a frazzle.
20. The boys wore their Boy Scout uniforms in the parade.

21. The lawn will have to be rolled in the spring.
22. The boys rolled up in a blanket for the night.
23. We had rolls just out of the oven for breakfast.
24. Put the emergency brake on so the car will not roll.

25. The house was sold at a good price without trouble.
26. I am sold on your plan for a vacation in the mountains.
27. The stock of merchandise was sold out in a few days.
28. We sold everything in the house at public auction.

29. Are you going to the Shore this summer?
30. Don't swim too far from the shore in the surf.
31. Our house is only one block from the shore.
32. The walls had to be shored up with heavy timbers.

33. Both doors were left open for fresh air.
34. We can take both of you home if you are ready.
35. I found both books interesting and worth reading.
36. Both of us were invited to ride in the procession.

37. Which road will get us home in the shortest time?
38. I will go with you as far as the crossroads.
39. We have to travel all the way over a country road.
40. The boys like to drive a roadster and drive it fast.

41. A group of boys loaf on the street corner every night.
42. A loaf of bread is smaller than ever and costs more.
43. Please buy a sandwich loaf for me when you are out.
44. We should have loaf sugar for the coffee at the reception.

45. Will you pour the coffee or the tea at the party?
46. It looks as if it is going to pour down rain.
47. The people poured out of the building at five o'clock.
48. She poured out her heart to me about her disappointment.

49. The oldest boy is the sole support of the family.
50. The sole of my shoes is worn out and needs repairing.
51. My sole purpose in coming to town was to see you.

52. The sport shoes have rubber soles to keep them from slipping.

53. There are five hundred rose bushes in bloom.
54. We have an old rosewood piano in the family home.
55. The rose window in the cathedral is beautiful.
56. Playing in the cold weather put roses in your cheeks.

57. Will you have toast with your coffee and eggs?
58. Toast your feet before the fire when you come in.
59. At the banquet we drank a toast to the President.
60. The children like to toast marshmallows over the camp fire.

124.   *Homophenous Words*

Sew, so, sow

  You should sew the seams on the machine.
  Some men can sew on their own buttons.
  I do not believe what you have told me is so.
  The wind was so strong I couldn't walk against it.
  It is time to sow the seed for our spring garden.
  We should sow those seed deep in the ground.

Doze, knows, noes, nose, toes

  You will feel better if you doze for a few minutes.
  It may be fatal to doze while driving a car.
  "Nobody knows the trouble I've had."
  Who knows all the rules of the road?
  How many noes were counted when we voted?
  I don't believe the noes are in the majority.
  Our horse unexpectedly won by a nose.
  The ship had to nose its way into the river.
  I am sorry if I stepped on your toes.
  The work is interesting and keeps us on our toes.

Road, roan, rode, rote, rowed, wrote

    The road runs past rich farm land.

    The road runs uphill all the way.

    The roan saddle horse is the best one to ride.

    Will you ride the roan or the bay mare in the race?

    We rode all day in a Greyhound bus.

    The children rode the ponies at the Fair.

    Some people learn everything by rote.

    We do not remember so well the things we learn by rote.

    Who rowed in the college crew?

    We rowed across the river for supplies.

    Who wrote the best book of the year?

    I wrote home every week I was away.

125.　　　　*Idiomatic Expressions and Adages*

Open	Mother welcomed me with open arms.
Soul	He couldn't call his soul his own.
Bones	He didn't make any bones about not liking the book.
Know	No one seemed to know how to break the ice.
Home	Home is where I hang my hat.
Post	I have gone from pillar to post hunting a job.
Whole	The news set the whole town by the ears.
Own	You are standing in your own light.
Bone	I have a bone to pick with you.
Those	Those people live from hand to mouth.
Low	Swing low sweet chariot, acoming for to carry me home.
Pose	Someone will have to pose for the picture of Miss Liberty.
Quota	Our team was the first to make its quota in the last Red Cross drive.

Hole   The shop is just a hole in the wall.
Coals   It is like carrying coals to Newcastle to do that.

LESSON XXII

Diphthong Long ī

126. For long *i*, as in "pie," the first movement is like that for *ah*, in "pa," the relaxed-wide; but for long *i*, this relaxed-wide movement is followed by a quick relaxed-narrow movement.

127.   *Contrast Words*

pipe-palm   light-lard
mice-mars   dine-darn
pike-park   I'm-arm

128.   *Practice Words*

mile	ripe	wire
fine	line	like
wipe	time	pipe
sight	kind	white
shine	while	sigh

129.   *Sentences*

1. We have to walk a mile to get the school bus.
2. The train is running seventy miles a minute.
3. The company owns a square mile of timber land.
4. We have passed the last mile post going home.

5. The pendant is worn on a fine gold chain.
6. The weather has been fine all this week.
7. The print is so fine it hurts my eyes to read it.
8. You will be fined for parking in that space.

9. You should wipe your hands dry in cold weather.
10. The dishes will dry without wiping if drained.
11. The windshield wiper on the car is out of order.
12. Be sure to wipe your shoes on the mat at the door.

13. We are almost in sight of home at last.
14. His eyesight is remarkable for his age.
15. The sight of the mountains made me happy.
16. Take careful sight before firing the rifle.

17. The sun shines in the south window of the house.
18. Someone should shine the children's shoes.
19. Some children shine in class more than others.
20. The furniture has been polished until it shines.

21. We like to let our fruit ripen on the trees.
22. The fruit will never get ripe in this weather.
23. The time seems to be ripe for a change in policy.
24. Do you know how to tell if a watermelon is ripe?

25. We must line up the children for the parade.
26. The actor forgot his lines and had to be prompted.
27. The boys were lined up for the foot races.
28. Some people follow the line of least resistance.

29. We had the time of our lives on the boat trip.
30. It is time for the morning mail to be distributed.
31. No one on the boat had a timepiece to go by.
32. It is high time we started for the long ride home.

33. What kind of weather are we going to have today?
34. Everyone in the neighborhood has been kind to me.
35. We found every kind of stone in the museum.
36. What kind of book do you want from the library?

37. It is a long while since we were last at home.
38. I will wait for you while you go to the store.
39. We had to while away two hours between trains.
40. It isn't worth while to read the story again.

41. The wire from the family gave us little information.
42. There are copper wire screens in all the windows.
43. The applicant will have to pull wires to get the job.
44. The farm house has been wired for electricity.

45. It looks like rain or snow this morning.
46. I like to walk in the snow when dressed for it.
47. Everyone thinks the boy looks exactly like his father.
48. What would you like to have as a special treat for dinner?

49. We pipe our water from the spring on the mountain.
50. The church has had a new pipe organ installed.
51. The water pipes will freeze in winter if not covered.
52. While downtown will you buy some tobacco for my pipe?

53. White clothes are best to wear in the tropics.
54. We could see only the whites of their eyes in the dark.
55. The snow in town does not stay white very long.
56. When will the White House be open to the public?

57. I gave a sigh of relief when the work was finished.
58. I like to hear the wind sigh through the pine trees.
59. We often sighed for home and family while in camp.
60. Why did you sigh when reading the story?

130. *Homophenous Words*

Fight, fine, vied, vine

　　We had to fight our way through the crowd.
　　Are you going to the prize fight tonight?

We had a fine view of the parade from the window.

How large a fine did you have to pay for speeding?

Two boys vied for the same place on the team.

No one vied with me for the appointment.

There is a beautiful vine growing over the porch.

The children have a grapevine swing over the brook.

Ride, right, rind, rite, write

Would you like to ride home with us?

The children like to ride the ponies.

We had the right of way at the crossing.

The school is right across the street.

We made spiced pickle of the watermelon rind.

I like the rind in orange marmalade.

Marriage is a rite of the church.

We watched a solemn rite on Sunday.

Be sure to write while you are away.

I had to write almost a book of explanation!

Cite, side, sighed, sign, sight, site

How many men in the regiment will you cite for bravery?

Can you cite chapter and verse for your statement?

You will have to get on the right side of the boss.

How many will side with us in the coming election?

We sighed for the good old times of other days.

You sighed while you were reading the story.

There isn't a sign of life about the place.

You will have to sign a contract before buying.

The old home was a sight for sore eyes.

The ship will soon be in sight of land.

We have found just the site for our new home.

No one likes the site chosen for the new school.

131.   *Idiomatic Expressions and Adages*

Advice   We should have advice and counsel.

Inviting	You are inviting trouble by making the trip.
Bygones	It is well to let bygones be bygones.
Time	It is time to be up and doing.
Climax	That last order caps the climax.
Line	He swallowed the story, hook, line, and sinker.
Shine	We will go on the trip rain or shine.
Rime	There is no rime or reason in the method.
Tide	Time and tide wait for no man.
Riding	That man is riding for a fall.

LESSON XXIII

Diphthong Long ā

132. For long *a*, as in "late," the first movement is like that for short *e*, as in "let," the extended-medium; but for long *a*, this extended-medium movement is followed by a quick relaxed-narrow movement.

133. *Contrast Words*

pay—pet	say—set
fay—fed	day—debt
way—wet	gay—get

134. *Practice Words*

mail	shape	chain
face	lame	make
way	name	fame
rain	wave	race
safe	same	cape

135. *Sentences*

1. Don't forget to mail my letters when you go out.
2. The mail is late today and I can't wait for it.

3. Please hold my mail until I return from the trip.
4. It is so late the letter should be sent by air mail.

5. Your face is very familiar but I forget your name.
6. We shall have to face the music and take our punishment!
7. As our house faces the west we see the sunsets.
8. The face of the country has entirely changed since I left.

9. Which way does the wind blow this morning?
10. We went home by way of the school to get the children.
11. Lead the way and we will follow wherever you go.
12. There is a right and a wrong way to do things.

13. It has rained every day this week.
14. You should take your raincoat with you.
15. The rain came in at the open window.
16. There was a beautiful rainbow after the shower.

17. The bridge was not safe after the flood.
18. We keep the bonds in the office safe.
19. Government bonds are a safe investment.
20. You are safe in making the statement.

21. Are you in shape to do such hard work?
22. We left everything shipshape in the house.
23. Our plans are shaping up very well.
24. The salad was molded in the shape of flowers.

25. You gave a very lame excuse for your absence.
26. You should use a cane when walking if you are lame.
27. I was very lame from the unusual exercises.
28. What is meant by a "Lame Duck" in Congress?

29. What is the name of the street you live on?
30. Can you name all the forty-eight states for me?
31. We can go with you on any day you name.
32. The name of your friend escapes me for the moment.

33. The waves broke over the bow of the boat.
34. Which shop gives the best permanent wave?
35. You will have to wave a flag to stop the train.
36. There is a wave of optimism sweeping the country.

37. I received the same gift last Christmas.
38. This is the same place we started from.
39. The food is always the same in this restaurant.
40. We are to spend our vacation at the same place.

41. Food is cheaper in the large chain stores.
42. Few men wear a watch chain nowadays.
43. The dress was made on a chain-stitch machine.
44. A strange chain of events caused the trouble.

45. Can you make up four tables of bridge this evening?
46. I am sure we will make better time on the subway.
47. It won't make any difference if you stay home.
48. We will have to make time for the appointment.

49. His fame as a painter is world-wide.
50. Would you rather have fame or fortune?
51. Fame does not always bring happiness with it.
52. Admiral Peary won fame by discovering the North Pole.

53. Are you going to the race track today?
54. We had to race to the station to meet the train.

55. The boys have trained and are in fine form for the race.
56. I had to race through the work to get off on time.

57. The fur cape is not very warm for a cold day.
58. The family spend their summers at their home on Cape
    Cod.
59. The ship sailed home by way of the Cape of Good Hope.
60. A cape is hard to keep on on a windy day.

136.   *Homophenous Words*

Ail, ale, hail, hale

Something seems to ail the baby this morning.
Does anything ail you that you cannot work?
Will you have a glass of ice cold ginger ale?
We had ale and Swiss cheese sandwiches for lunch.
I tried to hail a taxicab at the street corner.
A hail storm this afternoon ruined our garden.
The man is hale and hearty at seventy-five.
The police will hale the speeder into court.

Dale, nail, tail, tale

We tramped up hill and down dale on our hike.
Ferns were growing in the dale beside the brook.
What kind of nail polish do you like best?
Someone should nail down the board on the porch.
The airplane went into a tailspin before landing.
We were just in time to see the tail end of the play.
We were fascinated by the tale of the explorer.
The boys like to read a blood and thunder adventure tale.

Fade, fate, feign, feigned

The colors of the dress will fade in this sun.
I like to watch the colors fade from the sky.
It seems to be my fate to stay late at the office.

It is the irony of fate that it should rain today.
The children tried to feign innocence when caught.
It is useless for you to feign ignorance of the subject.
The laborer feigned illness to get out of work.
You know you feigned sleep while we were talking.

137. *Idiomatic Expressions and Adages*

Pace	We had to drive all the way at a snail's pace.
Make	You may make free with our papers if you wish.
Fade	It is time for me to fade out of the picture.
Name	Did I hear you taking my name in vain?
Weight	My opinion doesn't carry much weight, I'm afraid.
Sails	The report took the wind out of my sails.
Nails	Our landlord is as hard as nails.
Paid	You will be paid in your own coin.
Cake	You can't eat your cake and have it too.
Raise	I'll raise cane if I have to go away at once.

Lesson XXIV

Diphthong Oy

138. For *oy*, as in "boy," the first movement is like that for *aw*, in "paw," the puckered-wide; but for *oy*, this puckered-wide movement is followed by a quick relaxed-narrow movement.

139. *Movement Words*

buy bay boy
file fail foil—knife knave coif
rye ray Roy
side sail soil—dice days toys
line lain loin—aisle ale oil
tie day toy—kine cane coin

140. *Practice Words*

boy	toil	coin
foil	voice	oil
roil	moist	coil
soil	join	broil
boil	noise	

141. *Sentences*

1. The messenger boy will deliver the package.
2. There are three girls and one boy in the family.
3. When do the Boy Scouts have their next meeting?
4. The boys broke a window in the school playing ball.

5. The children have a large ball of tin foil.
6. Silver foil covers the back of the mirror.
7. The police were able to foil the burglars.
8. Do you know how to use the foil in fencing?

9. Be careful not to roil the water where we fish.
10. Some people roil me with their arguments.
11. Fish will not bite if the water has been roiled.
12. Someone has roiled the water in the pool.

13. The plants should have a very rich soil.
14. You will soil your white gloves on the bus.
15. We need to put several inches of top soil on the lawn.
16. The soil should be well fertilized in the spring.

17. The water for the tea must be freshly boiled.
18. The story of the kidnapping made my blood boil.
19. Be careful not to let the pot boil over on the stove.
20. You should boil the potatoes with the skins on.

21. The men toiled to the top of the mountain.
22. We have to toil from morning to night to earn a living.
23. We were caught in the toils of malicious stories.
24. The dressing table is covered with toilet articles.

25. Few people listen to the voice of experience.
26. His voice carried to the back of the auditorium.
27. No one has voiced a complaint about the arrangements.
28. The speaker's pleasant voice made it easy to listen to him.

29. The ground should be kept moist around the plants.
30. The palms of my hands are always moist in hot weather.
31. The air is full of moisture during the month of August.
32. Every eye was moist when the pathetic story was finished.

33. Will you join us for dinner after the theater?
34. Where does this road join the main highway?
35. How many members joined the club during the year?
36. We should join forces in our fight for good government.

37. There is so much noise I cannot hear what you say.
38. The noise of the traffic on the avenue kept me awake.
39. Did you hear the noise of the storm last night?
40. Some people make a lot of noise in everything they do.

41. Have you a coin for the telephone call?
42. That word was coined only recently.
43. How many silver coins have you in your purse?
44. Please don't jingle the coins in your pocket.

45. There is too much oil in the salad dressing.
46. Oil on the highway is dangerous for automobiles.
47. A new oil well has just been drilled on the property.
48. The electric fan should be oiled before using it again.

49. A coil of telephone wire is on the ground.
50. The hawser is coiled on the deck of the ship.
51. A few women still wear their hair in a coil.
52. The snake was coiled ready to strike.

53. Shall I broil the steak over the charcoal fire?
54. We served broiled chicken for luncheon.
55. The sun is so hot I feel as if I had been broiled.
56. You can broil the lamb chops under the gas.

142.   *Homophenous Words*

Noise, toys

There is too much noise in the room.

The noise of the airplane woke me up.

The firemen repair toys for the poor children.

He toys with the problem of changing his job.

Boys, poise

The boys are playing baseball in the back lot.

The boys will help with the farm work.

The speaker had a great deal of poise.

Your friend should acquire more poise.

DOUBLE CONSONANTS

Lesson XXV

Bl and pl

143.   *Practice Words*

bleak	blew	plant
black	bloom	play
blind	bluff	ply
block	please	plot
blow	pledge	place

144.   *Sentences*

1. This is a bleak part of the country.
2. The hill is bare and bleak in the winter.
3. The woman's face had a bleak expression.
4. There is a bleak view from the house.

5. The black clouds in the west mean a storm.
6. Your chimney is belching a lot of black smoke.
7. The black dress will be appropriate for the occasion.
8. Black shoes can be worn with almost any dress.

9. You seem to have a blind spot on some subjects.
10. The blinds in the house are all drawn down.
11. Please pull down the venetian blind to keep out the sun.
12. Are you sure the job will not be a blind alley?

13. We can walk as we are only one block from home.
14. The fallen tree will block the highway unless removed.
15. The baby loves to build houses with his blocks.
16. All the houses on our block are just alike.

17. The bad news was a blow to the family.
18. You should let the air blow through the house.
19. The blow fell without warning and was a shock.
20. People who like to blow their own horn are very boring.

21. The wind almost blew the house away in the storm.
22. We blew on our fingers to get them warm when we came in.
23. I nearly lost my hat when the wind blew it into the street.
24. I blew in to see the family for only a few minutes.

25. The roses bloom all summer in this climate.
26. The children have the bloom of health in their cheeks.
27. It is too early for the fruit trees to be in bloom.
28. Do you know what kind of bloom the plant has?

29. We watched the sailboats on the bay from the bluff.
30. The bluff overlooks the harbor and the shipping.
31. Everyone likes the man's bluff and hearty manner.
32. His bluff manner really hides a kind heart.

33. It is almost impossible to please some people.
34. Will you please help me with my schoolwork?
35. It will please us to have you see our new home.
36. What will please the children for Christmas?

37. Is that promise a sacred pledge?
38. You may make a pledge to the Red Cross.
39. Can you repeat the pledge to the flag?
40. I pledge my word of honor to pay you back.

41. You should plant the seed in the fall to get blossoms.
42. The superintendent took us through the food plant.
43. Plant your feet firmly on the ground and stand still.
44. Do you know the name of the plant we found in the woods?

45. It is important for everyone to have some play time.
46. She played the piano well for so young a child.
47. We are going with friends to see the high school play.
48. Are you going to play football on the varsity team?

49. The ship will ply between New York and Jacksonville.
50. The carpenter can ply his trade here if he is a Union man.

51. There is a three-ply rug on the floor in the dining room.
52. Everyone wanted to ply the speaker with questions.

53. The house is built on a large plot of ground.
54. The new novel has a most interesting plot.
55. No one is trying to plot anything against you.
56. We should have a plot of the entire neighborhood.

57. There is a place for one more in our car.
58. Where shall I place the vase of flowers?
59. We want you to visit us at our place at the Beach.
60. I don't know where to place your friend at the table.

145. *Homophenous Words*

Blush, plunge, plush

The story embarrassed me and made me blush.

At first blush we thought a mistake had been made.

We had to plunge into work when vacation was over.

A plunge into the ocean before breakfast will wake you up.

The furniture is upholstered in plush.

There are plush curtains at the door.

Black, blank, plank, plaque

The bootblack will shine your shoes.

The body of our new car is painted black.

Your expression was a complete blank when I spoke.

We shall need a blank book for our sales records.

You will have to plank down the money for the purchase.

The plank was wet and slippery after the rain.

There is a beautiful plaque hanging on the wall.

There is a picture of Mount Vernon on the plaque.

Bland, plaid, plan, planned, plant

You should use a bland ointment on your skin.

The climate here is bland and delightful.
The blouse is pretty with that plaid skirt.
She wore a plaid hat and handbag to match.
What is your plan for this afternoon?
We must plan the program for the next meeting.
I planned to go home for lunch but am too busy.
A large party has been planned for the holiday.
The men work in a large manufacturing plant.
It is time to plant the tulip bulbs.

146.   *Idiomatic Expressions and Adages*

Please	You may please yourself about the matter.
Blind	That is a case of the blind leading the blind.
Block	The boy is a chip off the old block.
Black	He bought the meat on the black market.
Plain	It is as plain as the nose on your face.
Plenty	When will there be peace and plenty in the land?
Bluff	He changed his mind when we called his bluff.
Blow	It helps to blow off steam once in awhile.
Play	It isn't always easy to play second fiddle.
Place	We were in a tight place when our plans were discovered.

Lesson XXVI

Br and pr

147.   *Practice Words*

breath	broad	private
break	brush	promise
branch	press	prepare
brim	print	produce
bright	practice	present

148.   *Sentences*

1. I have hardly been able to get my breath today.
2. It was so cold I could see my breath this morning.
3. There isn't a breath of air in this room.
4. The run for the bus made me short of breath.

5. We had to break away from the meeting early.
6. There seems to be a break in the rain clouds.
7. Some people seem to get all the breaks in life.
8. It is often hard to break away from traditions.

9. A branch of the tree fell down in the storm.
10. The town is on a branch of the railroad.
11. Who is manager of the branch store of the A & P?
12. The railroad branches off a mile from the station.

13. My cup of happiness is full to the brim.
14. The hat has a wide brim to shade my eyes.
15. Trees grow along the brim of the river.
16. The hat is made without a brim.

17. The dress is attractively trimmed with bright colors.
18. He is the brightest boy in his class at school.
19. The children's room should be bright and sunny.
20. The light is so bright I can't open my eyes.

21. Broadway in New York is many miles long.
22. The house is on a broad street in the suburbs.
23. We were pleased with the broad views of the speaker.
24. Did you listen to the President's broadcast today?

25. Someone should brush up the floor after dinner.
26. You should brush your hair before coming to the table.

27. We saw a rabbit and five little ones in the underbrush.
28. I am sure someone brushed past me in the dark.

29. The clothes must be pressed before wearing again.
30. Do you believe in freedom of speech and of the press?
31. We pressed the flowers in a book as souvenirs.
32. We had to press everyone at the office into service.

33. Be sure to print your name on the blank form.
34. The book is out of print and cannot be bought.
35. Some things we see in the papers should not be printed.
36. It is a good thing to have your fingerprints on file.

37. How long did you practice your lesson this morning?
38. The doctor has a very large practice in the city.
39. It is not always easy to practice what we preach.
40. He began the practice of law in a small town.

41. The soldier is a private, first class.
42. Where can we have a private conversation?
43. Can't you read? It says, "Private Property."
44. Do you prefer government or private ownership?

45. The student gives great promise as a teacher.
46. Our vegetable garden promises well this summer.
47. We should never fail to keep a promise to a child.
48. Will you promise me you will come another time?

49. It is time to prepare the children's lunch.
50. We must prepare for a long trip next week.
51. Have you prepared your lessons for tomorrow?
52. Everyone should prepare for a rainy day.

53. The farmer must take his produce to market.
54. Can you produce sufficient evidence to prove your case?
55. Our garden produces enough vegetables for the table.
56. The play will be produced entirely by home talent.

57. How many members of the club were present at the meet-
     ing?
58. The present you gave me is just what I wanted.
59. It is well to live in the present and the future.
60. The work cannot be done at present but will be done soon.

149. *Homophenous Words*

Bride, bright, brine, pride, pried

   The bride and groom are on their honeymoon.
   Fortunate is the bride the sun shines on.
   The bright lights almost blinded me.
   The child is not very bright in school.
   The soup is as salty as brine.
   The corned beef is still in the brine.
   The rose garden is our pride and joy.
   The teacher takes pride in her students' success.
   The burglar pried open the kitchen window to get in.
   I pried open the can with a coin from my pocket.

Braid, brain, brayed, prate, prayed

   The dress is trimmed with a bright color braid.
   The little girl wears her hair in a long braid.
   The brain was not injured in the fall on the ice.
   The problem is too much for my poor brain to solve!
   The donkey brayed when he saw us coming to feed him.
   The boys brayed like a donkey when pinning on his tail.
   Some people like to prate of their great learning.
   No one likes to hear a man prate of his wealth.

We prayed for the success of our venture.

The men on the life raft prayed for rescue.

Brace, braise, brays, praise, prays, preys

The workmen will have to brace the walls.

The hunter brought home a brace of birds.

You should braise that cut of beef to make it tender.

It will be better if the lamb is braised for dinner.

The donkey brays when he wants to be fed.

When the donkey brays at the gate I let him in.

We have only praise for the work you have done.

A word of praise is good for anyone's morale.

The minister prays too long and I get sleepy.

The penitent prays for forgiveness of his sins.

The lion preys on smaller animals for his food.

The mistake preys on his mind and makes him unhappy.

150.   *Idiomatic Expressions and Adages*

Bred	He was born and bred in a good home.
Break	We'll have to break away from the party.
Pride	Pride goeth before a fall.
Profit	It won't profit you to sell the house.
Bring	The announcement will bring them up short!
Bread	He doesn't know which side his bread is buttered on.
Pretty	Things have come to a pretty pass in this town.
Proceeds	Who will get the lion's share of the proceeds?
Prompted	What prompted you to go home early?
Bridge	Don't cross the bridge before you come to it.

LESSON XXVII
Fl and fr

151.   *Practice Words*

fleet	floor	frank
flag	flake	frost
float	freeze	free
fly	fresh	front
flower	frame	frown

152.   *Sentences*

1. The fleet has steamed into the harbor and can be visited.
2. The boy is very fleet of foot and will run in the race.
3. The company has a large fleet of trucks on the road.
4. How many boats does the yacht club have in its fleet?

5. We have to flag the train at this station.
6. The flag is flying from the mast on the Post Office.
7. The walk from the door to the gate is of flagstones.
8. We found the blue flag growing near the swamp.

9. Which float won the prize in the parade?
10. The boys like to dive from the float offshore.
11. The men will float the logs down stream in the spring.
12. The bank will float the loan for the new project.

13. We watched the birds fly south in the fall.
14. There is nearly always a fly in the ointment.
15. Would you rather fly home or go by train?
16. Trout fishermen like to make their own flies.

17. Have you seen this flower around here before?
18. She wore a red flower in her hair to the dance.

19. The flowers are blooming in profusion this spring.
20. We planted flowering shrubs beside the house.

21. The room has small rugs on a hardwood floor.
22. The apartment is on the fifth floor of the house.
23. The amount of work to be done almost floored me.
24. The diver walked on the floor of the ocean.

25. The paint has begun to flake off the house.
26. There were snowflakes in the air this morning.
27. The snowflakes are falling fast and melting as they fall.
28. The floor is covered with flakes of paint from the ceiling.

29. You will freeze without a coat in this weather.
30. We have a supply of meat in the deep freeze.
31. How long will it take to freeze the ice cream?
32. The freeze in Florida ruined the orange crop.

33. This fresh air feels good after that hot room.
34. We get fresh vegetables from a farmer's market.
35. A fresh wind is blowing from the west today.
36. We need a fresh point of view for our work.

37. The modernistic frame just suits the picture.
38. The plants were started early in a cold frame.
39. The framework of the house has been finished.
40. The man was a victim of a frameup by his associates.

41. I like people better if they are frank with me.
42. The letter can be sent in a franked envelope.
43. A frank statement from you will be appreciated.
44. The man's open, frank expression gave us confidence.

45. The paper says there will be a heavy frost tonight.
46. You should defrost the refrigerator this morning.
47. We are afraid the frost has killed the early fruit.
48. There was a hoar frost this morning when we got up.

49. Will you be free to help me this afternoon?
50. You will be free from interruptions here.
51. You are free to go and come as you please.
52. Some people are very free with their money.

53. There is a large, roomy house that fronts on the ocean.
54. You have spilled something on the front of your suit.
55. The dress buttons down the front and is easy to get into.
56. Park the car in front of the house until we are ready to go.

57. Some people always have a frown on their face.
58. Someone is sure to frown down every suggestion.
59. We shouldn't frown on the young people's fun.
60. The sun in my eyes made me frown when the picture was taken.

153.   *Homophenous Words*

Flick, fling

    Just flick the whip over the horse's back.

    Don't flick the cigarette ashes onto the rug.

    Why did you fling out of the room when I spoke to you?

    The children must not fling their clothes onto the floor.

Flour, flower

    You should use self-rising flour for the cake.

    You should flour the pan for the biscuit.

    I have never seen that flower before.

    The woods around here are full of this flower.

Friend, fret

What is the name of your friend?

A friend in need is a friend indeed.

Don't fret about what cannot be helped.

The invalid will fret if left alone too long.

154.   *Idiomatic Expressions and Adages*

Flesh	The story made my flesh creep.
Fling	The young people had to have their fling.
Flag	You should never lower your flag.
Free	You will be given a free hand in the work.
Fresh	She was as fresh as a daisy this morning.
Friday	Who is your Man Friday?
Flea	Someone put a flea in my ear.
Flip	Shall we flip a coin for it?
Flattery	So much flattery would turn anyone's head.
Frying	He jumped out of the frying pan into the fire.

LESSON XXVIII

Sl, sm, and sp

155.   *Practice Words*

sleep	smart	spell
slam	smoke	spirit
slide	small	span
slip	smile	spare
slight	smooth	speak

156.   *Sentences*

1. How many hours do you sleep each night?
2. I am sure a good night's sleep will fix you up.
3. I was so tired I slept the sleep of the just.
4. I fell asleep in the armchair while reading the paper.

5. Please do not slam the door when you come in.
6. I made a grand slam at bridge and won the game.
7. You shouldn't slam your books down on the table.
8. The wind will slam the door shut unless you prop it open.

9. The children like to slide on the ice on the pond.
10. The slide on the playground is popular with the children.
11. The engineer must have a slide rule to do his work.
12. Some people are able to slide through life without working.

13. The slip is too long for the dress you have on.
14. The ferry boat is just coming into the slip.
15. Be careful not to slip on the freshly waxed floor.
16. The plant will grow from a slip in wet sand.

17. There is only a slight chance of success.
18. The young girl has a very slight build.
19. I didn't mean to slight you at the party.
20. We have only slight evidence in the case.

21. You were smart to think of the answer so quickly.
22. The salt water made my eyes smart when in swimming.
23. The dress is a smart style and not very expensive.
24. Do you belong to the smart set in your town?

25. The room was full of smoke from the wet wood.
26. Smoking is not allowed in department stores.
27. What brand of cigarettes do you like to smoke?
28. Black smoke was pouring from the factory chimney.

29. This apartment is too small for our family.
30. I have only a small share in the business.

31. We could barely hear the child's small voice.
32. How often people say, "What a small world this is!"

33. Smile when you say that or take the consequences.
34. I hope you will smile with favor on the suggestion.
35. Your smiling face is always a welcome sight.
36. The President greeted his callers with a smile.

37. The water is as smooth as glass this morning.
38. Let me smooth the pillow under your head.
39. The letter may smooth the way for you abroad.
40. The grass on the golf course is as smooth as velvet.

41. I forget how to spell your name.
42. We are having a spell of bad weather for a change.
43. Let me take a spell at driving while you rest.
44. There are some people who never learn to spell correctly.

45. The employees showed a willing spirit.
46. The spirit is willing but the flesh is weak.
47. We kept the spirit of the law as well as the letter.
48. The boys have shown a wonderful school spirit.

49. Only one span of the bridge has been completed.
50. The work extended over a span of about five years.
51. The crack in the wall was as wide as a hand-span.
52. My father always drove a span of bay horses.

53. There isn't a spare room in the house.
54. Can you spare a little time for me this afternoon?
55. We had barbecued spare ribs and sauerkraut for dinner.
56. We do not believe that to spare the rod will spoil the child.

57. Why don't you speak to me when we meet?
58. Will you speak to our young people at their meeting?
59. What a man does and not what he says speaks for him.
60. The visitor could speak the language of the people.

157.   *Homophenous Words*

Slim, slip

    The dress was made for a slim young girl.

    The invalid has a slim chance for recovery.

    Would you like to have a slip from this plant?

    I shall have to slip out of the meeting early.

Smoke, spoke

    Black smoke is pouring in the window.

    Would you like to smoke while you are waiting?

    No one spoke to me at the meeting.

    We spoke of the friends back home.

Slab, slam, slap

    There is a marble slab on the table.

    Put a slab of salt pork in the baked beans.

    I heard the doors slam in the wind.

    We could hear you slam things around in the room.

    The remark was like a slap in the face.

    We saw a slapdash comedy at the movie.

158.   *Idiomatic Expressions and Adages*

Sleep	I shall have to sleep on the suggestion.
Sleeve	You must have something up your sleeve.
Slip	That was just a slip of the tongue.
Small	We were just small potatoes in the community.
Smart	The baby is as smart as a steel trap.
Smoke	Put that in your pipe and smoke it.
Spin	He can always spin a good yarn.

Split   That man will always split hairs in an argument.
Spare   Spare the rod and spoil the child.
Spirit   We had to spirit away the Christmas packages.

Lesson XXIX

Sn, st, and sw

159.   *Practice Words*

snow	stack	sway
sneak	stage	sweep
snap	stand	swim
snip	store	swing
steep	stall	swarm

160.   *Sentences*

1. There was an unusually heavy snowfall last night.
2. We are completely snowed under with work at the office.
3. The children have fun coasting and playing in the snow.
4. The farmers were snowbound for a week after the storm.

5. A sneak thief got into the store and stole the cash.
6. I tried to sneak away from the meeting before it was over.
7. I am sure I saw someone sneaking around the house.
8. The children like to sneak food out of the refrigerator.

9. The new job is a regular snap and it bores me.
10. The snapshot of the waterfall is a beautiful picture.
11. This cold snap is likely to ruin the fruit crop.
12. The snap on the lock of the kitchen door is broken.

13. Will you snip a piece of the material for me?
14. The child is just a little snip of a thing.

15. You will have to snip the thread and begin again.
16. May I snip off a lock of your hair to keep?

17. The price of the automobile is too steep for me.
18. It is hard to get up the steep hill near the house.
19. We tried to steep ourselves in the lore of the place.
20. You will have to steep the herbs for an hour.

21. There is a tall smokestack on the factory.
22. You may stack the wood in the garage if you will.
23. You will find the bookstacks in the back room.
24. I have a stack of letters to write before mail time.

25. The stage play was well done and very interesting.
26. This is the last stage of the long journey home.
27. The stage whisper could be heard all over the room.
28. George Washington traveled by stagecoach or on horse-back.

29. There is a taxicab stand at the next corner.
30. You may stand the umbrella on the porch to drip.
31. It is useless to argue for I will stand pat on what I said.
32. The house built one hundred and fifty years ago still stands.

33. Which is the largest department store in town?
34. Which store has the best fruit and vegetables?
35. The furniture will have to be stored while we are away.
36. You may store your things in our attic if you wish.

37. Be careful not to stall the engine in traffic.
38. The farmer has a vegetable stall in the market.

39. Someone should put the horse in the stall at once.
40. We must try to stall for time in signing the contract.

41. I like to watch the trees sway in the wind.
42. The speaker can sway the opinions of the crowd.
43. Do you know who holds sway in this town?
44. The children are under the sway of their teacher.

45. Someone should sweep the floor of the office.
46. We must make a clean sweep of the matter to the boss.
47. The storm will sweep through the town unless the wind changes.
48. The flood will sweep away the homes if the dam breaks.

49. I swim in the ocean every morning before breakfast.
50. Some people think they must always be in the swim.
51. Everything swims before my eyes from looking at the sun.
52. It is more refreshing to swim in salt water than in fresh.

53. We have a swing in the back yard for the children.
54. There is a grapevine swing over the brook.
55. The job is too big for me to swing alone.
56. The gate in the picket fence always swings open.

57. I am afraid the bees are going to swarm.
58. The ants swarmed all over the lump of sugar.
59. The boys swarmed over the farm on arrival.
60. People swarmed everywhere at the County Fair.

161.   *Homophenous Words*

Snack, snag

Everyone has gone to the snack bar for lunch.
We like to have a snack in the middle of the morning.

We ran the boat onto a snag in the river.

Be careful not to snag your stockings.

Stack, stag

The smokestack should be cleaned out before long.

I found a stack of mail on my desk when I returned.

How many men were in the stag line at the dance?

We saw a stag as we drove over the mountain road.

Staid, stain, stained, state, stayed

The new employee seems to be a very staid person.

She is a staid and precise person and never unbends.

There is a bad fruit stain on the tablecloth.

Boiling water is supposed to take out a fruit stain.

The evening sky was stained with crimson and gold.

The wood was stained mahogany before finishing it.

You will have to state your case again before the Board.

The salesman has been in every State in the Union.

The soldier overstayed his leave and was disciplined.

We stayed at home when it rained in the morning.

162. *Idiomatic Expressions and Adages*

Snap	That was just a snap judgment and unfortunate.
Snippy	Why were you so snippy when meeting your friend?
Snail	We had to walk all the way at a snail's pace.
Snake	My supposed friend proved to be a snake in the grass.
Stem	We couldn't stem the tide of resignations at the club.
Stage	There is nothing to be done at this stage of the game.
Swap	The men like to swap fishing stories in the evening.
Swayed	Some people are easily swayed by a speaker.

Swim   The story was so sad it made my eyes swim in tears.

Stale   I am growing stale on the job and want a vacation.

Lesson XXX
Dr and tr

163.   *Practice Words*

dream	drop	trim
draft	dry	true
draw	drain	trick
dress	treat	trust
drive	train	trouble

164.   *Sentences*

1. Some people cannot remember what they dream.
2. I didn't dream you would be here so early.
3. I think that is just one of your pipe dreams.
4. You should stop daydreaming and get your work done.

5. The draft from the window blows on my back.
6. How many men were taken in the draft during the war?
7. Who will draft the resolutions at the end of the meeting?
8. That is just a rough draft of the article I wrote.

9. You will have to draw your own conclusions.
10. Will you draw up the agreement for us to sign?
11. The children like to draw pictures at school.
12. The chimney draws well and throws out the heat.

13. You will not have time to dress before dinner.
14. How long will it take you to dress the children?

15. The new furniture will dress up the room.
16. Did the butcher dress the chicken for you?

17. Do you drive or take the bus to work every day?
18. You may leave the car in the driveway for awhile.
19. That man will drive a sharp bargain so watch him.
20. This noise will drive me wild if it keeps up.

21. I am sure I felt a drop of rain on my face.
22. You can drop the bags on the floor for the time being.
23. It is a long drop from the porch roof to the ground.
24. Be sure to drop in to see us sometime when in town.

25. The ground is so dry this summer nothing will grow.
26. The clothes will soon be dry in this hot sun.
27. The sermon was so dry and uninteresting I went to sleep!
28. This spell of dry weather is lasting a long time.

29. The drain will carry off the water from the basement.
30. You should drain off all the water from the lettuce.
31. The swamp land will have to be drained this summer.
32. The vacation trip put a big drain on our bank account.

33. We gave the children a treat of ice cream and cake.
34. This is my treat so I'll pay the bill for lunch.
35. You should not treat the matter under discussion so lightly.
36. The evening at the opera was a big treat for us.

37. What time does the train leave for the West?
38. When does the football team begin to train?
39. You should begin at once to train your successor.
40. My train of thought was interrupted when you spoke.

41. The trees should be trimmed in the spring.
42. The new suit is trim and becoming to you.
43. We shall have to trim our expenses for a few months.
44. You will have to trim the edges of the walks and lawn.

45. The story has been proved true in every respect.
46. The students this term are running true to form.
47. The newspapers gave a true picture of what happened.
48. Is it true that you are changing your position?

49. The boys are always up to some trick.
50. Do you have any parlor tricks to entertain us?
51. I was tricked into buying the goods and regret it.
52. You have taken every trick in this rubber.

53. I would trust that man anywhere, under any circumstances.
54. Her father left her a trust fund for life.
55. I trust you understand the business and can carry on.
56. The child was entrusted to the care of the conductor.

57. There seems to be some trouble here; what is it?
58. It is never any trouble to help you if you need it.
59. Some people are always in trouble about something.
60. We have never had any trouble with our new car.

165.   *Homophenous Words*

Drays, trace, trays
      The drays are loaded and ready to leave.
      How many drays does the company have in use?
      We can't find a trace of the paper you want.
      The children like to trace pictures on rainy days.

There were trays of food on the table.

Where are the trays in the cafeteria?

Drain, trade, train, trait

The water does not drain off the road very well.

The drain in the basin seems to be stopped up.

Small boys like to trade their possessions.

The trade name of the firm has commercial value.

The baseball team will soon begin to train.

We took the streamline train to California.

The boy's strongest trait is dependability.

What is the characteristic trait of the new employee?

Drab, dram, tram, tramp, trap

The dress is very drab and unattractive.

The family live in a drab part of the town.

You are to take one dram of the medicine.

A dram is about one teaspoonful.

The tramcar going to town was crowded.

Coal in the mines is often hauled in a tramcar.

We are going for a tramp in the woods this afternoon.

We took a trip to South America in a tramp ship.

Are you trying to trap me with your questions?

We have set a trap for the mice in the cellar.

166.   *Idiomatic Expressions and Adages*

Draw   You can draw your own conclusions about the story.

Drive   The buyer will drive a hard bargain if he can.

Drug   The material is a drug on the market today.

Trumped   That is a trumped-up excuse and a poor one.

Tree   I'm afraid you are barking up the wrong tree.

Drop   Be sure to drop me a line while you are on vacation.

Dry   We were left high and dry at the railroad station.

Drum	Someone will have to drum up trade for our Fair.
True	The statement in the paper doesn't ring true.
Tracks	We made tracks for home when we saw the storm coming.

LESSON XXXI

Cl and gl

167.   *Practice Words*

clean	clock	glad
clap	close	glide
clear	class	glimpse
climb	glance	glow
clip	glare	gloomy

168.   *Sentences*

1. We must clean house before the warm weather comes.
2. Someone must clean the fish for supper.
3. The clean clothes are ready to be put away.
4. You might as well come clean and tell the truth.

5. I just heard a clap of thunder and saw lightning.
6. The children like to clap their hands to music.
7. I clapped my hand over my mouth to keep from laughing.
8. There was just time to clap everything into the suitcase.

9. The weather will soon clear up and we can leave.
10. We had a clear view of the stage from the balcony.
11. Will you clear the dishes from the table after supper?
12. We drove clear across the country on our vacation.

13. We climbed to the top of the mountain for the view.
14. It was a steep climb up the mountain but worth it.
15. At bedtime the children climb on my lap for a story.
16. You will have to climb the stairs to the third floor.

17. We drove over the new highway at a fast clip.
18. Someone should cut the grass and clip the hedge.
19. Please don't clip my hair too short in the back.
20. He clips his words so it is hard to understand him.

21. The clock is running slow and should be regulated.
22. The silk stockings have pretty clocks on each side.
23. I like to hear the grandfather clock chime the hours.
24. My alarm clock flashes a light and wakes me up.

25. The horse race was so close everyone was excited.
26. The air in the room is very close and unpleasant.
27. That man is close-mouthed about all his affairs.
28. It is close to time to stop working and go home.

29. Will you be able to enter the Junior Class at college?
30. The package was sent to you by third class mail.
31. We traveled first class on the ship going to Europe.
32. The spirit of this year's class is really wonderful.

33. Will you glance over the papers before you leave?
34. I saw you glance at me as I passed your desk.
35. The ball glanced off the pitcher's glove and dropped.
36. We gave the parade just a passing glance as we passed.

37. The glare from the headlights blinded me.
38. Why were you glaring at me when I looked up?

39. We found a glaring mistake in the report submitted.
40. There was a glare of ice on the street this morning.

41. The children are glad to be home from camp.
42. The speaker was given a glad hand at the meeting.
43. We were glad to see our friends again after so long a time.
44. This is a glad day for us with everyone at home again.

45. The dance step is just a glide and easy to learn.
46. The boat glides through the water like a swan.
47. We watched the glider make a flight from the hill.
48. There is a glider on the side porch if you like it.

49. We caught a glimpse of you as you passed the house.
50. I glimpsed the mountains in the distance from the train.
51. We were able to get a glimpse of the family last week.
52. All I want is a glimpse of the book to see if I like it.

53. We sat in the glow of the firelight and talked.
54. The praise for my work made me glow with pleasure.
55. We watched the afterglow of the sunset from the porch.
56. The children's cheeks glow with health from playing out-doors.

57. This house is dark and gloomy on a rainy day.
58. Some people always have a gloomy outlook on life.
59. We went out of doors as the gloomy room was depressing.
60. Turn on the lights as this is such a gloomy day.

169.   *Homophenous Words*

Class, glass
    Some people are very class-conscious.
    The beginners class is very small this year.

The plate glass window was broken in the storm.

A glass of water is on the table beside the bed.

Clam, clamp, clap

The family has gone to the beach for a clambake.

We had clam chowder for dinner every day.

The clamp on the box is broken and must be mended.

A clamp had to be put on the warped table top.

The clap of thunder was so loud it frightened me.

The police will clap the prisoner into a cell.

Cloud, clout, clown

It is beginning to cloud up and looks like rain.

That black cloud rolling up means a wind storm.

The highwayman will clout his victim if he can.

We had to put a clout on the axle of the wheel.

The clown at the circus amused the children.

The boys like to clown when playing together.

170. *Idiomatic Expressions and Adages*

Class	The family belongs to the working class.
Clean	You will have to come clean about the loss.
Clay	He was like clay in the hands of his friends.
Climber	My neighbor is a social climber and a snob.
Clapped	I haven't clapped my eyes on the family for ages.
Close	We had a close shave in the accident.
Glide	We tried to glide out from under the work.
Glad	I dressed in my glad rags for the party.
Globe	The family has been globe trotting for a year.
Glow	There was a glow of pleasure on her face.

LESSON XXXII
Cr and gr

171.   *Practice Words*

cream	crisp	ground
crease	crank	group
credit	green	grain
craft	grate	grant
cramp	grind	grown

172.   *Sentences*

1. The farmer has sold the cream of his crop.
2. Will you have cream and sugar in your coffee?
3. Shall I cream the sugar and butter for the cake?
4. The material is a cream white slipper satin.

5. This material will not crease or wrinkle.
6. The rain took the crease out of the trousers.
7. Fold the material on the crease when putting it away.
8. The dress is badly creased and needs pressing.

9. The bank has refused to give credit to the merchant.
10. Where will I find the Credit Department of the store?
11. We should be careful to give credit where credit is due.
12. I hope you give me credit for having more sense!

13. We enjoyed our lessons in handcrafts.
14. The workman's craftsmanship is remarkable.
15. You will find the workman as crafty as a fox.
16. What kind of craft can sail on the river?

17. The house is too cramped for comfort.
18. Cramp the wheels of the car before leaving it.
19. The cold weather made my muscles cramp.
20. You will have writer's cramp if you sign those letters.

21. The air is cold and crisp and very bracing.
22. The pie crust is crisp and flaky and delicious.
23. French fried potatoes should be brown and crisp.
24. Be sure the crackers are crisp before serving them.

25. We had to crank the first automobiles by hand.
26. The children have been indoors and are cranky today.
27. I am sure the letter was written by some crank.
28. We found the crankcase in the car was broken.

29. The grass on the lawn is just turning green.
30. The apples are green but just right for applesauce.
31. The house is painted white with green shutters.
32. The green workman is rapidly learning his trade.

33. The carrots should be grated for the salad.
34. There are some voices that grate on me.
35. There is an iron grating over the basement window.
36. There is a glowing fire in the grate in the living room.

37. The knife was sharpened on a grindstone.
38. The children love to hear an organ-grinder.
39. We grind fresh coffee each morning for breakfast.
40. The work is just a steady grind and uninteresting.

41. Where shall I throw the coffee grounds?
42. The ground is covered with snow this morning.

43. The butcher ground the hamburger steak for me.
44. It is too early to plow the ground for a garden.

45. The pictures should be grouped in one room.
46. The picture of the family group is good of everyone.
47. Group the children around the piano for some songs.
48. The group was interested in the plan we suggested.

49. The grain of the wood in the panel is beautiful.
50. What kind of grain can you grow in the field?
51. You cannot buy grain alcohol without a prescription.
52. There is not a grain of truth in the story in the paper.

53. I hope you will grant my request and help us.
54. I am willing to grant you may be right this time.
55. Where is the Tomb of President Grant in New York?
56. The land-grant was signed by Patrick Henry in 1792.

57. The children have grown very fast this summer.
58. The vegetables were all grown in our garden.
59. We have grown accustomed to the climate and don't mind
     it.
60. What kind of fruit do you think can be grown here?

173.   .*Homophenous Words*

Crime, grime, gripe

        It is a crime to waste so much food.
        A crime has been committed in the name of justice.
        I must wash the grime of the city off my hands.
        We found dust and grime all over the place.
        It won't do any good to gripe about the work.
        There is always someone around to gripe about things.

Crib, crimp, grim, grip

>The corn crib has been filled to overflowing.
>
>The baby's crib is away from the window and drafts.
>
>The order puts a crimp in my plans for a day off.
>
>You should crimp the edges of the pie crust.
>
>Someone will have to carry my grip for me.
>
>You should always grip the handrail when going downstairs.
>
>Why do you look so grim about the news item?
>
>The accident was a grim affair for everyone concerned.

Crab, cram, cramp, grab, gram

>I had a soft shell crab and French fries for lunch.
>
>Did you ever use a crab for fishing bait?
>
>The student had to cram for final examinations.
>
>We can't cram another thing into the suitcase.
>
>I don't want to cramp your style by staying around.
>
>Get up and stamp your foot if you have a cramp in it.
>
>The bus franchise is a big grab by the company.
>
>You should not grab things away from the baby.
>
>A gram of distilled water was called for.
>
>The chemist used a gram of salt in the formula.

174. *Idiomatic Expressions and Adages*

Crack	That was a hard nut to crack.
Crazy	My grandmother's crazy quilt is on the bed.
Credited	I credited you with better sense than that.
Cradled	She cradled the flowers in her left arm.
Crossed	The thought never crossed my mind.
Crown	I hope success will crown your efforts.
Grand	We made a grand tour of the West.
Green	You must have a green thumb the way flowers grow.

Ground	We got in on the ground floor on the deal.
Grind	The mills of the gods grind slowly, but they grind small.

LESSON XXXIII
Qu (Sound of kw)

175. *Practice Words*

quick	quaint	quantity
quiet	quite	quarter
quote	queer	question
queen	quality	quiz

176. *Sentences*

1. The boy has a very quick mind and learns rapidly.
2. We shall have to make a quick change of plans.
3. The quicksilver is worn off the back of the mirror.
4. The remark you made cut me to the quick.

5. The house was quiet all day with the children away.
6. The couple had a quiet wedding in the bride's home.
7. Will you see if you can quiet the baby for me?
8. We spent a quiet vacation with the family on the farm.

9. Please don't quote me to the newspapers.
10. Can you quote the authority for the statement?
11. The newspaper quotes market prices for the week.
12. You should use quotation marks around the statement.

13. The queen bee is still in the hive.
14. She walks into the room like a queen.
15. I held three queens in my bridge hand.
16. Who was queen of the Apple Blossom Festival?

17. The costume was very quaint and won a prize.
18. We drove through a quaint part of the country.
19. She was dressed in quaint old-fashioned clothes.
20. We were interested in the quaint customs of the place.

21. I am not quite ready to leave for the office.
22. It is quite a long time since we were home.
23. You are quite right in your statement of what happened.
24. I'm afraid the rain is not quite over for the day.

25. There are queer-looking clouds in the west.
26. Who is the queer person we just passed?
27. That move will queer everything for us.
28. We saw a queer-looking automobile on the street.

29. That meat is the finest quality we have.
30. Some people are a poor judge of quality.
31. Make sure of the quality of the material before buying.
32. The material is of poor quality and won't wear well.

33. We bought a quantity of vegetables at the market.
34. You will need only a small quantity of butter.
35. How large a quantity of sugar should we have?
36. It is quality rather than quantity that counts.

37. It is now a quarter past five and time to start dinner.
38. The apples should be cut into quarters for the pie.
39. The people here come from all quarters of the country.
40. It is a quarter of a mile to the country store.

41. You haven't answered the questions in my letter.
42. Do you question my judgment or will you trust me?
43. I question the truth of the statement that was made.
44. It seems as if the children ask a million questions.

45. There will be a quiz in mathematics tomorrow.
46. I never like to be quizzed about personal matters.
47. The quiz was too hard for me and I failed it.
48. I was ill and stayed home the morning of the quiz.

177.   *Idiomatic Expressions and Adages*

Quality	Those folk are real quality.
Queen	Everything was done to the queen's taste.
Queer	You will queer my job if you are not careful.
Quick	Jack be nimble, Jack be quick, Jack jump over the candlestick.
Question	I would never question your word.
Quits	We'll have to cry quits as we can't agree.
Quiz	It won't do any good to quiz me.
Quotes	The sentence should be in quotes.

Lesson XXXIV

Thr, shr, and str

178.   *Practice Words*

thread	shrink	string
thrift	shred	strain
thrive	shrewd	straight
throw	shrug	strike
through	shrill	stroke

179.   *Sentences*

1. I can't thread the needle without glasses.
2. The suit is almost threadbare from long wear.
3. The thread is not strong enough for the material.
4. There is a thread of truth in the story you heard.

5. I am sending the clothes to a thrift shop.
6. Where shall I find thrift dresses for sale?
7. It is smart to be thrifty even in times of plenty.
8. We made money on the thrift shop at the club rooms.

9. The store does a thriving business.
10. The flowers will thrive in this weather.
11. The invalid will thrive in this climate.
12. The children thrive on fresh air and sunshine.

13. Don't throw old clothes away; give them away.
14. I had to throw my clothes on in a hurry.
15. You shouldn't throw up your job without good reason.
16. The ocean is only a stone's throw from the house.

17. How soon will you be through for the day?
18. We walked through the woods all morning.
19. I looked through the papers for the story.
20. I hope your plan for a vacation will go through.

21. How much will the material shrink when washed?
22. Do you shrink from meeting strangers?
23. The blanket will not shrink if properly washed.
24. The dress shrinks every time it is washed.

25. There isn't a shred of truth in the statement.
26. Will you shred the cabbage for the coleslaw?
27. That report would tear his reputation to shreds.
28. There is just a shred of material for a sample.

29. The salesman gave me a shrewd glance.
30. The real estate man was too shrewd for me.

31. I don't like the man's shrewd business methods.
32. He is a shrewd businessman who should be watched.

33. I want an answer, not a shrug of the shoulders.
34. That is one you can't shrug off so easily.
35. Some people have a habit of shrugging.
36. What did you mean by that shrug of the shoulders?

37. The shrill whistle of the boat made me jump.
38. Her voice is very shrill when she is excited.
39. The child's voice is shrill and very penetrating.
40. The bird shrilled his cry outside my window.

41. The fisherman brought in a string of fish.
42. There are no strings attached to the gift.
43. The string of pearls broke in the street.
44. We have a patch of string beans in the garden.

45. The gravy will have to be strained before serving it.
46. I heard a familiar strain of music coming from the church.
47. Be careful not to strain your back when lifting the bag.
48. We had to strain every nerve to finish the work in time.

49. The children were told to come straight home from school.
50. It was hard to keep my face straight when I heard the story.
51. We got the story straight from the family and it is true.
52. We drove for miles over a long stretch of straight road.

53. Do you think they will strike oil on the farm?
54. We must leave for home when the clock strikes three.
55. The men in the factory are out on strike for more pay.
56. Were you able to strike a bargain with the builder?

57. That was a stroke of good luck for the family.
58. Who is stroke of the college crew this year?
59. We are leaving town on the stroke of midnight.
60. A stroke of lightning hit the club house.

180.   *Homophenous Words*

Threw, through

    Someone threw a ball against the house.

    We threw the accumulation of old papers away.

    When will you be through your work for the day?

    We went through the art museum in one afternoon.

Strain, straight, strained, strait, strayed

    I am beginning to feel the strain of the work.

    You should strain the orange juice for the baby.

    It is hard to keep to the straight and narrow path.

    The witness told a straightforward story.

    We strained the fruit juice for the jelly.

    The relations with the chief were strained.

    We sailed through the Strait of Gibraltar.

    Our neighbor seems to be a strait-laced person.

    The baby has strayed away from home.

    We strayed into a political meeting.

181.   *Idiomatic Expressions and Adages*

Shrinks	He shrinks from meeting strangers.
Shrimp	He is a little shrimp of a fellow.
Shred	There isn't a shred of truth in the news item.
Strings	The boy is tied to his mother's apron strings.
Strike	You should strike while the iron is hot.
Stroke	That was a stroke of good luck.
Thread	There was a thread of truth in the statement.
Threw	We threw discretion to the winds.

Thrift   We gave the clothes to a thrift shop.
Throat   The story gave me a lump in the throat.

Lesson XXXV

Spl and spr

182.   *Practice Words*

splash	splotch	spring
splice	splint	sprinkle
split	spread	spry
splurge	spray	sprout

183.   *Sentences*

1. Be careful not to splash the water on the floor.
2. The other car splashed mud on the car windows.
3. We had to splash through the mud puddle in the road.
4. The painters left a splash of paint on the floor.

5. The rope will have to be spliced to make it reach.
6. Can you splice the wall boards and make them do?
7. The minister will splice the young couple.
8. The cable was short and spliced in two places.

9. Someone will have to split the logs for firewood.
10. There has been a split in the membership of the club.
11. I thought my head would split with all the noise.
12. Will you split your vote or vote a straight ticket?

13. We splurged in furnishing our new home.
14. Don't splurge when you move to a new place.
15. We do not like people who splurge and make a show.
16. We are going to splurge on our summer vacation trip.

17. There is a splotch of ink on the paper.
18. The painter left a splotch of paint on the window.
19. There are splotches of color on the wall paper.
20. Her face was splotched with red from excitement.

21. The chair has a splint bottom and straight back.
22. The broken arm was put into splints by the doctor.
23. When will you get the splints off your broken leg?
24. The doctor used a plaster cast instead of splints.

25. Spread the clothes on the grass to bleach them.
26. Will you spread the children's bread with jam?
27. My grandmother wove the bedspread by hand.
28. We must be careful not to spread the rumor.

29. It is time to spray the trees in the orchard.
30. Put the spray of dogwood in a vase on the table.
31. The spray from the waves came over the boat.
32. The children like to stand under the lawn sprayer.

33. Do you like to dive from the springboard?
34. The springs on the car are not very strong.
35. Will you help me spring the tire into the rim?
36. This is a perfect spring day for a tramp in the woods.

37. It has just begun to sprinkle and will soon rain hard.
38. I must sprinkle the clothes to get them ready to iron.
39. There is just a sprinkling of flowers in the field.
40. I am sure this sprinkle will not amount to anything.

41. The old man is very spry for his advanced age.
42. You'll have to be spry if you get the train.

43. This weather doesn't make me feel very spry.

44. Do you use Spry in your cooking or some other shortening?

45. There are new sprouts on the plant.

46. The seeds have just begun to sprout and will soon be up.

47. We had Brussels sprouts for dinner with roast pork.

48. The beans are so old they have begun to sprout.

184.   *.Homophenous Words*

Splint, split

> We learned to make splint baskets in class.
>
> The splint-bottom chair was very old.
>
> It will be all right to split your vote.
>
> The work will be split up and distributed.

Sprig, spring

> We rooted a sprig from the plant.
>
> I put a sprig of lavender among my handkerchiefs.
>
> Spring is very late this year.
>
> We get our water from a mountain spring.

185.   *Idiomatic Expressions and Adages*

Splash	The new president made a big splash.
Spliced	Where can the couple get spliced?
Split	We can split the difference later.
Splurge	We will splurge when our ship comes in.
Spread	There was a wonderful spread at the reception.
Spree	Let's go on a spree when we get a raise.
Springs	Do you believe that man springs from monkeys?
Sprinkling	There was a sprinkling of children at the movies.
Sprout	We'll have to sprout some new ideas.
Spruce	You must spruce up before going out.

Giving Him One Better

1. The train was pulling out of the station when a young man threw his bag onto the observation platform and swung himself up over the handrail. He stood panting but triumphant as the train gathered speed.

An elderly man on the platform observed him with some scorn. "You young fellows don't keep yourselves in good condition," he snorted. "Why, when I was your age I could carry a cup of coffee in one hand, run half a mile, catch the 8:15 by the skin of my teeth, and still be fresh as a daisy."

"You don't understand, Pop," puffed the young man. "I missed this train at the last station."

Efficiency

2. An applicant for work at the Ford plant asked a veteran Ford employee if it were true that the company was always finding methods of speeding up production by using fewer men. The veteran replied:

"Most certainly. In fact," he continued, "I just had a dream which illustrates the point. Mr. Ford was dead and I could see the pallbearers carrying his body. Suddenly the procession stopped. Mr. Ford had come to life. As soon as the casket was opened he sat upright and, on seeing six pallbearers, cried out at once: 'Put this casket on wheels and lay off five men.'"

He Got His Character

3. A company promoter advertised for an office boy. His final choice fell upon a bright youth to whom he said: "My boy, I like your appearance and manner. I think you may do for the place. Did you bring a character?" "No, sir," replied the boy, "but I'll go get it." "Very well; come back tomorrow morning and if it is satisfactory I probably will employ you."

Late that afternoon the financier was surprised by the return of the young man. "Well," he said cheerfully, "have you got your character?"

"No," answered the boy, "but I've got yours and I am not coming."

His First Patient

4. The small son of a physician, together with a friend, was playing in his father's office while the doctor was out making calls on his patients, when suddenly the doctor's son threw open a closet door and nearly frightened the small friend to death by showing him an articulated skeleton.

When the small friend was recovered the doctor's son explained that his father was very proud of that skeleton.

"Is he," asked the friend. "Why?"

"I don't know," was the answer, "maybe it was his first patient."

No Shop Talk Today

5. This incident occurred some time before the war, on a ship where gunnery crews were uncommonly keen. So much interest developed that it got to the point where the men did nothing but "talk shop." The commanding officer finally issued a ruling that there should be no "shop talk" during mess.

At the first meal after the order was posted, an attitude of obvious restraint prevailed. Every man was trying consciously to keep the conversation in general channels. When the chaplain arose to give the prayer, an officer touched him on the arm, warned solemnly: "Remember, Chaplain, no 'shop talk' today."

JUNIOR AT THE MOVIES

6. Like many young couples, this one made the mistake of bringing Junior to the movies. The infant saw no reason why he should be quiet, but the manager did.

"If you can't keep the kid quiet," the manager whispered harshly, "I'll have to ask you to take your money back and leave."

Promptly the baby went to sleep.

The movie went on and turned out to be one of those interminable, boresome productions. The husband shifted uneasily in his seat and finally nudged his wife.

"For goodness' sakes," he moaned, "give Junior a punch!"

HIS HELPFUL FORD

7. A gentleman who was visiting his lawyer for the purpose of making his will, insisted that a final request be attached to the document. The request was that the family Ford be buried with him after he died. His lawyer tried to make him see how absurd this would be, but failed, so he asked the man's wife to use her influence with him. She did the best she could, but she also failed.

"Well, John," she said finally, "tell me why you want your Ford car buried with you."

"Because I never got into a hole yet but what my Ford could get me out," was the reply.

THE SEWING CIRCLE

8. The Sewing Circle was talking about what the speaker had said.

One of the women said he was talking about the zoo. "I heard him say something about the reindeer."

"Oh, no," another dear lady said, "he was talking about the weather; he said, 'Has it rained here?'"

"I think you are all wrong," said the musician, "the speaker was saying he was a musician; he said he had a trained ear—I heard him distinctly."

"No," said another, "I agree with the first speaker, but I thought he said a trained deer."

"You are all wrong," said the hostess, "the speaker said to his wife, 'Are you ready for the train, dear?'"

One Way to Solve a Problem

9. This note was sent to a teacher by a mother to explain why her boy was not in school:

"Dear Ma'am: Please excuse Johnny today. He will not be in school. He is acting as timekeeper for his father. Last night you gave him this example: If a field is four miles square, how long will it take a man walking three miles an hour to walk two and a half times around it? Johnny ain't no man, so we had to send his daddy. They left early this morning, and my husband said they ought to be back late tonight, though it would be hard going. Dear Ma'am, please make the next problem about ladies, as my husband can't afford to lose the day's work. I don't have no time to lose, but I can spare a day off occasionally better than my husband can."

The Only Way

10. The father lectured his young son on the evils of fighting as a way of settling disputes.

"Don't you know that when you grow up you can't use your fists to settle an argument?" the father began. "You must begin to use peaceful and amicable means of arriving at a decision.

Try to reason things out. Try to discover by logic and evidence which is right; and abide by the right. Remember that might does not make right; though the strong may win over the weak, that still does not prove that the weak is wrong."

"I know, Dad," said the boy kicking at the grass, "but this is different."

"Different? How different? What were you and Johnny arguing about that had to be fought over?"

"Well, he said he could whip me and I said I could whip him, and there was only one way to find out."

Hill Was the Name

11. One man said to his friend, "I have an awful time catching people's names when I am introduced to them."

"So do I," said his friend, "but I have found a clever way to get around asking to have the name repeated. I just ask if the name is spelled with an *e* or an *i*. It usually works splendidly.

The first man said he had heard about that before, and it worked with him, too, until once he met a girl he wanted to know better, and now she wouldn't even look at him.

"Why is that?" asked the friend.

"Well, when I was introduced to her I didn't catch her name, so I asked whether she spelled it with an *e* or an *i*."

"What was the name?" asked the friend.

"Her name was Hill."

Cooperation

12. A man on the south side of town advertised his car for sale. Early the next morning a man who lived across the street came over and said: "Pardon me, but I see by last night's paper you advertised your car for sale."

"Quite true," said the man who advertised the car, "but surely you are not in the market for it."

"No," was the reply, "but I only live across the street and I also want to sell my car. And there would be no need of my spending my money for an advertisement if after the people were through looking at your car you could just send them across the street to look at my car."

A Bargain in Chickens

13. A farmer ordered a crate of live chickens to be sent to him by express. He went to the railroad station to get them and found that the crate was badly broken. However, he loaded it on the back of his truck and started home.

He was turning into his own courtyard when the truck jounced over a large hole in the road. There was a terrible squawking, and stopping the car, the farmer looked around to see his chickens disappearing in all directions. He jumped out of the car and started after them. After chasing chickens for several hours all over his own farm and the farm across the road, he found he had twenty-two.

He wrote to the man from whom he had ordered the chickens and complained. Almost by return mail he had a reply that said:

"You were lucky to find twenty-two. I sent only twelve."

Judge for Yourself

14. A noted eastern judge while visiting in the West went to church on Sunday; which isn't so remarkable as the fact that he knew beforehand that the preacher was exceedingly tedious and long-winded to the last degree. After the service the preacher met the judge in the vestibule and said:

"Well, your Honor, how did you like the sermon?"

"Oh, it was wonderful," replied the judge. "It was like the peace and mercy of God."

"Oh, I scarcely hoped to achieve that," said the minister much flattered. "How can you make such a comparison?"

"Why, very easily," replied the magistrate. "It was like the peace of God because it passed all understanding, and, like his mercy, I thought it would endure forever."

GETTING AT THE TRUTH

15. "Oh, mamma!" Willie rushed breathlessly into the parlor and stood panting before his mother. "A great big brown bear chased me all the way home from school."

"Oh, Willie," said the mother reproachfully, "you mustn't tell mamma a story like that."

"That isn't a story," denied Willie vigorously. "If you don't believe it you can look for yourself. It's still right outside our yard. I was scared 'most to death for fear it would eat me before I could get in."

The mother walked to the window. "Willie Brown," she said sternly, "go straight into the bedroom and kneel down and ask God to forgive you for that story. I see the big dog that chased you," she said sternly.

In a few minutes Willie came out of the bedroom smiling amiably.

"Did you ask God to forgive you?" inquired his mother.

"Yessum, I did; and God said, 'Never you mind about that, Willie; I thought that big dog was a bear myself until I got another good look at him.'"

THE POOR WOMEN

16. The gray-haired old beggar had chopped his quota of stove-wood and the kind lady had admitted him to the kitchen for his meal. She was an inquisitive person, and while the tramp made away with the food placed before him, she set up an endless line of questioning.

"And what was your occupation before you fell into this sad condition, my man?" she asked.

"I was a sailor, mum," said the bum between mouthfuls.

"Oh, a sailor. Well, you must have had some exciting adventures then?"

"That I did, mum. Why, once, mum, I was shipwrecked on the coast of South Africa, and there I came across a tribe of wild women who had no tongues."

"Mercy!" exclaimed the inquisitive woman. "Why, how could they talk, then?"

"They couldn't mum," replied the man, reaching for his hat and the last piece of bread on the plate, "that's what made them wild."

Without Professional Assistance

17. A lady who lives on a plantation in the southern part of Alabama went up to Birmingham on a visit. Upon her return an old Negro man who occasionally did odd jobs for her dropped by to welcome her home and to tell her the news of the neighborhood.

"Whilst you wuz gone Aunt Mellie died," he said. Aunt Mellie was a poor old colored woman who lived in a tumbledown cabin half a mile away.

"Oh, that's too bad," said the white lady sympathetically. "How long was she sick?"

"Jes' three or fo' days," he said.

"What ailed her?"

"They didn' nobody know. One mawnin' she up and fell sick and she kep' on gittin' wuss and wuss 'twel de fo'th day come and den all of a suddenlak she hauled off an' died."

"Who was the doctor?"

"She didn' have no doctor—she died a natchel death!"

THE TWO BROWNS

18. There were two Browns in the village, both of them fishermen. One lost his wife and the other his boat at about the same time. The minister's wife called, as she supposed, on the widower, but really called upon the Brown whose boat had gone down.

"I'm sorry to hear of your great loss," she said.

"Oh, it ain't much matter," was the philosophical reply. "She wasn't up to much."

"Indeed!" said the surprised lady.

"Yes," continued Brown, "she was a rickety old thing. I offered her to my mate, but he wouldn't have her. I've had my eye on another for sometime."

And then the scandalized lady fled.

THE STORY OF A BOY

19. "Your son is subnormal," said the teacher to Tommy's mother, "he will not profit by attending school. Better teach him to do odd jobs around the house. He is three years behind boys of his age."

"I know that Tommy is slow," replied his mother, "but he is intelligent. I do not consider him as hopeless as you do."

The mother took her boy away from that school and put him in another. It was a different kind of school; no entrance examination; kindly attention. One of the teachers in the school noticed that the boy liked poetry.

"Do you know much poetry?" she asked him.

"I know a good many poems," Tommy replied shyly, "and sometimes I write one down. Here's one I think is pretty good." The boy turned his pockets wrong side out revealing odds and ends of things and a crumpled piece of paper. He smoothed the paper out and began to read: "The curfew tolls the knell of parting day"—and on to the end. The boy was Thomas Gray. Not one word of Gray's "Elegy" was ever changed. It is considered perfect poetry.

A Girl Already Picked Out

20. The small town boasted a female preacher. One day while working in her study she heard a timid knock at her door. Answering the summons she found a bashful young farmer on the step.

"Good afternoon," the woman minister remarked. "Was there something that I could do?"

"Does the minister live in this house?"

"Yes, sir."

"Yes? Well, I calculate on getting married."

"All right; I can marry you."

The lady parson was no sight for sore eyes, and the young rustic glanced once at her face. Then, without comment he jammed on his hat and hurried down the walk.

"Will you be back?" the minister called.

"You ain't got no chance to marry me," he answered over his shoulder. "I don't want you; I already got me a girl picked out."

Not Contagious

21. Bobby ran to his mother all out of breath with the news that the lady next door had a new baby and she was awful sick.

His mother merely replied, "Yes, Bobby."

Bobby said, "You'd better go over to see her, Mummy, 'cause she's awful sick in bed."

And his mother said, "I know, I'll go over tomorrow, perhaps, when she is a little better."

"But she's so sick today," Bobby insisted, "that you ought to go right away, Mummy."

"Still, I think I'd better wait until she is a little better."

Bobby couldn't understand his mother's unwillingness to go at once. Finally the cause of his mother's unwillingness to go seemed to dawn on him, for he burst out:

"You don't need to be afraid, Mummy, it ain't catching."

THE POWER OF A LIE

22. A certain famous preacher, when preaching one Sunday in the summertime observed that many of the congregation were drowsing. Suddenly, then, he paused, and afterward continued in a loud voice, relating an incident that had no connection whatever with the sermon. This was to the following effect:

"I was once riding along a country road. I came to a house of a farmer and paused to observe one of the most remarkable sights I have ever seen. There was a sow with a litter of ten little pigs. This sow and each of her offspring had a long curved horn growing out of the forehead between the ears."

The clergyman again paused and ran his eye over the congregation. Everybody now was wide awake. He thereupon remarked:

"Behold how strange! A few minutes since, when I was telling you the truth, you went to sleep. But now, when you heard a whopping lie, you are wide awake."

WHO'S A GOAT?

23. The little girl was deeply impressed by the minister's sermon about the separation of the sheep and the goats when one gets to heaven. That night after she had gone to bed she was heard sobbing, and her mother went to her to ask what was the matter.

"It's about the goats!" Barbara confessed at last. "I'm so

afraid I am a goat, and so I'll never go to heaven. Oh, I'm so afraid I am a goat."

"My dear," the mother assured her sobbing child, "you're a sweet little lamb. If you were to die tonight you would go straight to heaven." Her words were successful in quieting the little girl, and she went to sleep.

But the following morning Barbara was found crying again in her bed, and when the mother appeared she wailed:

"I'm afraid about the goats."

"But mother has told you that you are a little lamb and you must never worry over being a goat."

The little girl was by no means comforted, and continued her sobs.

"Yes, Mamma," she declared softly, "I know that. But I'm afraid, awful afraid you're a goat!"

Get Your Handkerchief Out

24. It was in the Union Station, about six o'clock in the evening. An old woman sat on a bench wiping the tears from her eyes. A man walked in, stopped and studied her, then walked over and quietly asked her a few questions.

He turned and strode to the center of the station. "Gentlemen," he called out, "here is a poor old woman who wants enough money to take her to relatives in Denver. I'm a poor man but I'll start her off with a ten dollar bill. What will you gentlemen do?" Off came his derby, the ten dollar bill was placed inside, and the hat was soon half full of contributions ranging from a number of greenbacks to a lot of silver change.

Two of the men counted the money, and proceeded to present the grateful woman with more than a hundred dollars.

A man on the outside of the crowd came up to the one who owned the derby and had started the collection. "Why, hello, Banks—isn't this you?"

"Of course."

"And isn't that old woman your wife?"

"Yes, sir." He bowed elegantly. "Isn't it a poor husband that won't give his wife a ten dollar bill to help her to get off on a visit!"

A Hearty Welcome

25. A minister of a fashionable church had always left the greeting of strangers to be attended to by the ushers, until he read the newspaper articles in reference to the matter.

"Suppose a reporter should visit our church?" said his wife. "Wouldn't it be awful?"

"It would," the minister admitted.

The following Sunday evening he noticed a plainly dressed woman in one of the free pews. She sat alone and was clearly not one of the flock. After the benediction the minister hastened and intercepted her at the door.

"How do you do?" he said, offering his hand, "I am very glad to have you with us."

"Thank you," replied the young woman.

"I hope we may see you often in our church home," he went on. "We are always glad to see new faces."

"Yes, sir."

"Do you live in this parish?" he asked.

The girl looked blank.

"If you will give me your name and address my wife and I will call on you some evening."

"You wouldn't have to go far, sir," said the young woman, "I'm your cook."

This Is Not a Beehive

26. On their bridal tour the young couple went, as so many young couples do on their bridal tours, to Washington. They stopped at one of the larger hotels. For two days they did the usual sight-seeing stunts. They visited the Capitol and the White House and they crossed over to Arlington and they ascended the Monument.

Early on the morning of the third day the husband remained in the room to write some letters. The bride ran out to do a little shopping. Half an hour later she returned. She had left the elevator at her floor and was passing through the long hallway when she discovered that she had forgotten her own room number. She was sure, though, she knew which was the right door, but, when she turned the knob and tried to enter she found it locked.

She rapped on the panel.

"Let me in, honey," she said. "I'm back."

There was no reply.

She rapped again.

"Honey, oh, honey!" she called, "I want to get in."

From the other side of the door came the voice of a strange man—a dignified and an austere voice:

"Madam, this is not a beehive; it is a bathroom."

The Lady Made Good at Last

27. There was a Down-East housewife who, for years, was troubled with heart seizures. At the most inopportune times she would drop unconscious and after appearing for awhile to be at her last gasp would rally, and after an hour or so, seemingly would be as well as she ever had been.

The frequency of these attacks naturally interfered with her husband's labors and also was highly disturbing to his peace of mind. As he worked in his woodlot, or his meadow, or about his barn he never knew when the hired girl would be coming at full speed breathlessly to tell him his wife had suffered another stroke and surely now was on the point of death.

If his patience frayed under repeated alarms of this sort the worthy man gave no outward sign. Whenever the summons came—and it came very often—he would drop whatever he was doing and hasten to the house, invariably to find the sufferer on the way back to consciousness.

One hot day he was hoeing his potato patch when word arrived by messenger that the invalid had just had an especially violent attack. He rushed to the cottage.

The form of his wife was stretched upon the kitchen floor where she had fallen. A glance told him that this time she had made a go of it. Beyond question, life was gone.

"Well," he said, "this is more like it!"

THESE POOR RELATIONS

28. The conductor of a freight train sitting in the cupola of his caboose one day observed a tramp crawling up over a box car.

"Say," he said to the brakeman down in the caboose, "there's a bum down there on the sixth car. Run down and pitch him off."

The brakeman crawled out over the caboose and started running down over the tops of the cars. When he reached the car the tramp was on he yelled:

"Look here, Bo, I've come down here to kick you off, and I don't want no argument."

The tramp pulled a big .44 out of an arm holster, saying:

"Dat's all right, buddy. I got a little friend here what does all my arguing for me."

This wasn't so good so the brakeman returned to the caboose.

"Well, did you throw him off?" asked the conductor.

"Naw. He turned out to be a cousin of mine," said the brakeman, "and a man can't kick his own relative off the train."

"Then I'll go down and throw him off," said the conductor viciously.

He ran down over the cars, and in a few minutes he came back and took his place in the cupola.

"Well, did you throw him off?" asked the brakeman.

"Naw; he turned out to be a cousin of mine, too."

The Adulterated Truth

29. A young New Bedford couple got married and directly after the ceremony they left for a honeymoon trip through the southern states. When they arrived in a resort village in the Blue Ridge Mountains they decided to stay for a short while at a summer hotel. Immediately after their arrival they employed a colored man to look after their baggage, the bridegroom giving explicit instructions about removing all the rice and labels from their trunks so that no one would know that they were newlyweds. He tipped the Negro generously to insure against that worthy letting the news leak out that they were just recently married.

Two or three days later, whenever the bride left her room she noticed that everyone rushed to get a view of her. She informed her husband of the guests' strange actions and he, feeling sure the Negro baggageman had broken his word, called the latter to his room.

"What does this mean, Sam? I told you to be very particular about not letting any of the guests discover that we were just recently married. We have told no one. You were the only other person who knew. Now how does it happen that everyone gapes at us when we pass, and that all those old girls out on the front porch are continually whispering when we appear?"

"Honest to goodness, boss, I ain't tole nobody a-tall dat you-uns was jes' married. De fac' am, boss, dat I tole 'em de opposite, I tole 'em you-uns wa'nt married a-tall, but was jes' good friends."

The Naked Truth

30. Routine in the office of an eminent bone and muscle specialist went on with almost machine-like regularity. The famous doctor had a highly efficient corps of attendants who directed the stream of patients through the inner offices.

One morning a young, neatly dressed chap appeared in the doctor's reception room. In answer to the query of the nurse in charge, the youth said he wished to see the famous surgeon privately.

"Have you an appointment?" asked the nurse.

"No."

"Then this is your first visit?"

"Yes."

"Then go into that dressing room there, remove all your clothing, even to your shoes and sox, and wrap a sheet around you. When you have finished, or shortly after, a bell will ring twice. That will be your signal. Enter Dr. Blank's office through the door in the dressing room marked 'Office.'"

"But—" the boy blushingly began to protest.

The nurse in charge stopped him with a gesture.

"If you really want to see the doctor you must conform to the rules which he has set down. He does not modify them for anyone."

Still murmuring protests, the boy allowed himself to be hustled into the dressing room where he began to disrobe. After a short while the signal came and he opened the door and tripped across the sill into the famous doctor's office, clad only in the sheet and a few beads of perspiration.

"Well," the doctor barked, as the youth came into the room, "what's the matter with you?"

"There isn't anything the matter with me, Doc," answered the new arrival.

"Well, what in blazes are you doing in my office?"

"I came," said the boy, "to see if you'd care to renew your subscription to Collier's Magazine."

THE TIME KEEPER

31. In an important damage suit, a Negro witness for the man who had been injured testified that five minutes elapsed between the two events. Since the interval of time was very important, the opposing lawyer questioned the Negro's accuracy and sought to impeach him.

"You're sure it was five minutes?"

"Ain't I said so, suh?"

"Mightn't it have been four minutes, or three?"

"I said five minutes, boss."

The lawyer smiled unpleasantly. "Five and a half, say—or six minutes—or ten?"

"I done tole you exactly five minutes."

The lawyer leaned back with something of a sneer. "I'm going to test you right here and now. When I give the word, I want you to start timing—and then at the end of five minutes you tell me." The lawyer laid his watch down in front of him so that the witness could not possibly see it. "All right now, go ahead. At the end of five minutes you tell me."

The courtroom stilled into sudden interest at this unexpected test. The minutes ticked quietly by; many a person in the courtroom furtively examined his or her own watch, with one eye on the placid face of the witness.

At the exact end of five minutes the old Negro spoke up, "Dar's five minutes, perzackly, boss."

The lawyer grunted in disgust. "You were right for once."

The evidence so impressed the jury that the lawyer lost his

case. After all left the courtroom the lawyer came over to the witness. "Tom, I'll forgive you if you tell me just how you did it."

"Yes, suh, boss," said the witness agreeably, "I jus' figured it out."

"Figured it out?"

"Yes, suh. By de clock on de wall behin' you!"

For Heaven's Sake

32. The following story dates back to the last century. A number of lawyers, it is told, were dining in a tavern in the Indian frontier one day when a native came in and asked the landlord for something to eat. The landlord informed him that he would have to wait until the gentlemen were finished with their meals.

"Let him dine with us," suggested one of the lawyers to his companions, "and we will have some fun with him."

"You were born in this country?" asked one.

"Yes, sir, I was born in Indiana."

"Is your father living?"

"No, sir, he is dead."

"What was his occupation?"

"He was a horse-trader."

"Did your father ever cheat in his trades?"

"I reckon he did cheat many, sir."

"Where do you suppose he went when he died?"

"To heaven, sir."

"Has he cheated anyone there?"

"He has cheated one person there, I believe."

"Oh, he has! Then why didn't that person prosecute your father?"

"Well, he did want to, but he looked all over heaven and he couldn't find a lawyer."

An Exception for a Native Son

33. The clannishness of the rural Vermonter is proverbial. In illustration of this trait a distinguished citizen of the Green Mountain State told this story. He said that on a rather cloudy day a typical group of natives sat on the porch of the main general store in a town on the shores of Lake Champlain. Among them appeared a youth citified as to dress and having an air of assurance about him. In silent disapproval and, most disapprovingly of all, he had the confident manner of the alien.

"Good morning, everybody," he said breezily.

The elder of the group, a venerable gentleman, made answer for the rest:

"How' do," he said shortly.

Somewhat abashed at the coolness of his reception, the young man tried again:

"Looks rather like rain," he said.

" 'Twon't rain," said the old man in a tone of finality.

"But I rather thought from the looks of the clouds . . ."

" 'Twon't rain," repeated the ancient in the voice of one who is not used to being argued with.

A discouraging silence ensued. The stranger fidgeted in his embarrassment. The old man fixed him with a cold and unfriendly eye.

"What mought your name be?" he inquired, as though desirous of properly to classify a curious zoological specimen.

"My name is Nelson—Herbert Nelson," stated the youth.

"Nelson, hey?" said the old man. "There used to be some Nelsons out in the Kent neighborhood. Don't s'pose you ever heard of them."

"I've been hearing of them all my life," said the young man.

"I come from New York, but my father's name was Henry Nelson and he was born out near Kent in this county."

"Then you must a-been a grandson of the late Ezra Nelson," said the aged Vermonter. His manner perceptibly had warmed; indeed, by now it was almost cordial.

"Yes, sir," said the youth. "Ezra Nelson was my grandfather."

"Dew tell, now!" said the old man. "So you're a son of Henry Nelson and a grandson of Ezra Nelson? Well, in *that* case it may rain."

THE UNLIGHTED LANTERN

34. An old colored man, who had been crippled in the railroad service, served for many years as a watchman at a grade crossing in the outskirts of an Alabama town. By day he waved a red flag and by night he swung a lantern.

One dark night a colored man from the country, driving home from town, steered his mules across the tracks just as the Memphis flier came through and killed him and his team and wrecked the wagon. His widow sued the railroad for damages. At the trial the chief witness for the defense was the old crossing watchman.

Uncle Gabe stumped to the stand and took the oath to tell the truth, the whole truth, and nothing but the truth. Under promptings from the attorney for his side, he proceeded to give testimony strongly in favor of the defendant corporation. He stated that he had seen the approaching team in due time and that, standing in the street, he had waved his lantern to and fro for a period of at least one minute. In spite of the warning, he said the deceased had driven onto the rails.

Naturally, the attorney for the plaintiff put him to a severe cross-examination. Uncle Gabe answered every question readily and with evident honesty. He told just how he had held the lantern, how he had swung and joggled it and so forth and so on.

After court had adjourned the lawyer for the railroad sought out the old man and congratulated him upon his behavior as a witness.

"Gabe," he said, "you did splendidly. Weren't you at all nervous on the stand?"

"I certainly was, boss," replied Uncle Gabe. "I kept wondering what was going to happen if that white gentleman should ask me if that lantern was lighted."

STUMPY JOHN SILVER

35. Stumpy John Silver was a homing pigeon, hatched January 1918, just behind the battle lines in France. He received his early training in action, and carried military messages before he was many months old. In fact, he was one of the most active pigeons in the Army, and very skillful in keeping clear of a barrage.

On October 21, 1918, this carrier pigeon was released at Grand Pré with a message for headquarters, twenty-five miles away. The enemy was bombarding before the attack and the pigeon circled through the fire, finally getting his bearings. Men in the trenches saw a shell explode near the pigeon; the concussion tossed the pigeon up and then down. He regained altitude with great difficulty and continued on his course. Twenty-five minutes later the pigeon arrived at headquarters. The bird was a terrible sight; a machine gun bullet had pierced his breast; bits of shrapnel had ripped his tiny body; and his right leg was missing. The message tube was hanging to the ligaments of his leg. Nursing restored his health and he became a war hero, being named for the peg-legged man in Robert Louis Stevenson's "Treasure Island."

Stumpy John Silver was retired in 1921, and was assigned to the 11th Signal Company, U.S. Signal Corps, at Honolulu. He died in 1935 when he was almost eighteen years old. The name "John Silver" is called at every roll call of the 11th Signal Company and the senior non-commissioned officer present responds: "Died of wounds received in battle in the service of his country."

Stumpy John Silver's body is stuffed and is in the Aeronautical Museum at Wright Field, Dayton, Ohio. The little stuffed pigeon's body was presented to the Museum by the Chief Signal Officer, Signal Corps, United States Army.

SUPPLEMENTARY MATERIAL

I. Colloquial Forms

187. *How Long*

How long has it been raining?
"   "   do you think it will rain?
"   "   since we have had rain?
"   "   does the rainy season last?
"   "   before pay day?
"   "   since we were paid?
"   "   must we work before we are paid?
"   "   is the street?
"   "   a walk to school do the children have?
"   "   is the train?
"   "   before the mail comes in?
"   "   shall I wait for you?
"   "   must we wait between trains?
"   "   have you been waiting for me?
"   "   will you be at home?
"   "   may we work in the Library?
"   "   am I allowed to keep the books?
"   "   shall we stay at the ranch?
"   "   before breakfast will be ready?
"   "   has the President been in office?
"   "   before the car will be repaired?
"   "   do we have for a rest period?
"   "   will it take you to dress?
"   "   before the train will start?

How long does the train stop at this station?
"   "   have you been away?
"   "   before I shall see you again?
"   "   have you lived in this town?
"   "   was the French examination?
"   "   since you were in Europe?
"   "   does our President hold office?
"   "   did World War II last?
"   "   is the Lincoln Highway?
"   "   do your friends plan to stay?
"   "   before I shall see you again?
"   "   should I wait for you?
"   "   is the Mississippi River?
"   "   does it take you to get home?
"   "   will the meeting last?

188.   *How Much*

How much money have you earned this week?
"   "   have you saved this year?
"   "   has been paid on the bill?
"   "   had you hoped to make on the sale?
"   "   is the automobile to cost?
"   "   should be put aside for expenses?
"   "   was left over from dinner?
"   "   will the trip cost us?
"   "   water shall I put on the plants?
"   "   do you want to give to the Fair?
"   "   help can we get from the home office?
"   "   am I to pay for the radio?
"   "   money will you take with you?
"   "   food should we take on the picnic?
"   "   time must I spend on the job?
"   "   does the doctor charge?

How much do we need from the market today?

    "   "   is there in the Christmas fund?

    "   "   was in the bank at the end of the month?

    "   "   furniture will we have to buy for the house?

    "   "   rain has fallen this summer?

    "   "   ice cream should I buy for the party?

    "   "   time can you spare for a conference?

    "   "   will you charge to wash the car?

    "   "   time will it take to finish the job?

    "   "   damage did the storm do?

    "   "   much bread do we need for sandwiches?

    "   "   money can you save each week?

    "   "   ground has been ploughed?

    "   "   rain have we had this month?

    "   "   time did it take to do the work?

    "   "   oil does the well produce?

    "   "   snow is left on the ground?

    "   "   coal has been mined this week?

    "   "   cream do you like in your coffee?

    "   "   water do you drink every day?

    "   "   should I pay for a pound of butter?

    "   "   is the fare on the bus?

    "   "   insurance did you collect for the accident?

    "   "   sugar shall I put in the pudding?

    "   "   water is left in the well?

189.   *How Far*

How far have we driven since morning?

    "   "   is it to San Francisco?

    "   "   are we to travel by boat?

    "   "   was the car parked from the curb?

    "   "   will you walk with me?

    "   "   away can you see the mountains?

How far from home will we be this summer?
"   "   can we go by subway?
"   "   will we be allowed to drive on this road?
"   "   must we walk to the golf club?
"   "   had you gone when the messenger found you?
"   "   is it to the public market?
"   "   can you see in the dark?
"   "   could I trust that man?
"   "   may we venture into the woods?
"   "   do you want me to carry your bag?
"   "   out in the river should we go to fish?
"   "   is it to the North Pole?
"   "   will his voice carry?
"   "   does the bus go on this street?
"   "   may we walk through the woods?
"   "   does the train go without stopping?
"   "   must the workmen carry the lumber?
"   "   were my instructions carried out?
"   "   will you take us in the car?
"   "   shall we walk along the road?
"   "   can we go on this road?
"   "   is it from Boston to Washington?
"   "   shall we drive before stopping for the night?
"   "   do you live from the village?
"   "   did you swim this morning?
"   "   is this drawing out of proportion?
"   "   can you drive on one gallon of gasoline?
"   "   away can you read the sign?
"   "   will this bus take me?
"   "   do you have to go for groceries?
"   "   from home had the children strayed?
"   "   up on the beach does the water come at high
         tide?

How far away is the nearest gas station?
　"　　" from the curb is the car parked?

190.　　　　　　　　*How Many*

How many telephones are in the office?
　"　　" letters have been written?
　"　　" children does the family have?
　"　　" cars are parked in the driveway?
　"　　" boats are on the river?
　"　　" floats will be in the parade?
　"　　" guests have been invited?
　"　　" days are in February this year?
　"　　" miles are we from the airport?
　"　　" employees are on vacation?
　"　　" houses will be ready for inspection?
　"　　" rooms is the house to have?
　"　　" people can be accommodated for the night?
　"　　" trains will run each day in the summer?
　"　　" books can I take from the Library?
　"　　" people were on the beach today?
　"　　" oranges shall I buy?
　"　　" fish did you catch this morning?
　"　　" cars pass the house in one hour?
　"　　" were at church this morning?
　"　　" can you take in your car?
　"　　" rooms at the hotel have a private bath?
　"　　" people are expected at the convention?
　"　　" tables of bridge will there be?
　"　　" miles have we gone since morning?
　"　　" stripes on the American flag?
　"　　" apples will I need for the pie?
　"　　" Christmas presents did you receive?
　"　　" sheep were sent to market?

How many houses on the block are for rent?
   "   "   guests does the hotel accommodate?
   "   "   baths are on the second floor?
   "   "   new books have you read?
   "   "   letters did you write today?
   "   "   presidents of the United States have we had?
   "   "   bachelor presidents have we had?
   "   "   mistakes were made in the report?
   "   "   cars are in the garage?
   "   "   pencils should I buy?
   "   "   children are on the playground?

191.   *How Soon*

How soon will you be home?
   "   "   do you want your lunch?
   "   "   should we start for the train?
   "   "   must the garden be planted?
   "   "   will the tomatoes be ripe?
   "   "   does the picture start?
   "   "   have you planned to clean house?
   "   "   were you expecting a reply?
   "   "   shall I expect you home?
   "   "   is school to open in the fall?
   "   "   do you think the roses will bloom?
   "   "   should the field be plowed?
   "   "   can I have my laundry?
   "   "   will the bridge be finished?
   "   "   are you planning to take a vacation?
   "   "   will the parade get under way?
   "   "   shall we light the fire?
   "   "   will the mail be delivered?
   "   "   can you finish the work?
   "   "   will the hotel open for the summer?

How soon must the house be closed for the winter?

"   "   do you think we will have frost?

"   "   do the stores open on Saturday?

"   "   soon can we plant the garden?

"   "   should we start for home?

"   "   do you think it is going to rain?

"   "   will you be ready to go home?

"   "   should we start for the meeting?

"   "   can you give us a report?

"   "   does the train for New York leave?

"   "   shall we look for you?

"   "   were you to report for duty?

"   "   is the house to be painted?

"   "   did they say the pictures will be ready?

"   "   can I have your reply?

"   "   do you think it will begin to rain?

"   "   must the books be returned to the library?

"   "   should the corn be planted?

"   "   will the mail be delivered?

"   "   after dinner can we go in swimming?

"   "   is the circus coming to town?

"   "   can you report for duty?

"   "   must I file my income tax return?

192.   *How Hard*

How hard is the ice cream?

"   "   have you tried to get a job?

"   "   did you find the work?

"   "   should I make the examination?

"   "   am I expected to work for wages?

"   "   is the caramel candy?

"   "   the ground is this summer!

"   "   do you think the tires should be?

How hard it is to open these doors.

"   "   a bed do you like to sleep on?

"   "   was it to climb the mountain?

"   "   is it raining now?

"   "   shall I boil the eggs?

"   "   did you try to get to work on time?

"   "   are the stairs to climb?

"   "   shall I make the frosting on the cake?

"   "   was it to understand me over the phone?

"   "   does the water seem to be?

"   "   is the water on the farm?

"   "   should the driveway be before it is used?

"   "   will the trip be for the children?

"   "   was it to drive through the traffic?

"   "   are we expected to work?

"   "   did you find it to meet requirements?

"   "   was the lesson assignment?

"   "   did you fall on the ice?

"   "   is the work on the farm?

"   "   a mattress do you like to sleep on?

"   "   shall we freeze the ice cream?

"   "   should we work for the Fair?

"   "   have you found the job?

"   "   must the gelatine be before putting in the fruit?

"   "   does he work to support the family?

"   "   did you find the study of mathematics?

"   "   was it to find the house?

"   "   were the music lessons for you?

"   "   is the wind blowing now?

"   "   a pencil do you like to use?

"   "   did you try to get away?

"   "   will it be to move the furniture?

"   "   was it to handle the crowd?

How hard do you want your eggs boiled?
"   "   did the children try to fool you?

193.   *What*

What time do you get up in the morning?
"   does the paper say about the weather?
"   store is the most reliable?
"   book would you like to read?
"   time does the train leave?
"   brand of coffee shall I buy?
"   kind of work will I have to do?
"   bus passes the house?
"   shall I use for money?
"   is the news this morning?
"   is the name of this town?
"   can I do to help you?
"   do you know about the accident?
"   did the President say in his speech?
"   time shall I meet you?
"   President of the U. S. never married?
"   book do you want from the Library?
"   is the name of the author?
"   make of car do you drive?
"   kind of gasoline do you prefer?
"   shall I do next?
"   have you been doing with yourself?
"   are the prospects of success in the new venture?
"   have the newspapers said about the matter?
"   would you like for lunch?
"   day are you coming back?
"   time does the boat sail?
"   kind of position are you looking for?
"   do you do if you see a pin?

What have you done with your time?
    "   would you like for Christmas?
    "   magazines do you like to read?
    "   is the smallest state in the United States?
    "   work must be done first?
    "   did you ask me to do for you?
    "   will the material cost?
    "   time will we have lunch?
    "   book are you reading now?
    "   part of town is growing fastest?
    "   lamp do you want turned on?
    "   did the paper say about the weather?
    "   is the matter with you today?

194.   *Why*

Why should I do all the work?
    "   is the room so dark?
    "   did you go to town this afternoon?
    "   did the workmen go home so early?
    "   is the mail so late?
    "   has the front door been left open?
    "   were the books not returned before?
    "   have I been chosen to represent the club?
    "   is everyone so late for the meeting?
    "   are the buses always so crowded?
    "   didn't you tell me before?
    "   were you so late tonight?
    "   did you put the car in the garage?
    "   do you have so much luggage?
    "   don't you get a porter to carry the bags?
    "   has the subway stopped running?
    "   did you go away and leave me?
    "   were the children allowed to go home alone?

Why does the water have such a queer taste?
"   must you leave so soon?
"   do you look at me that way?
"   would you like to change jobs?
"   can owls see in the dark?
"   are the lawns so brown?
"   have you turned on the lights so early?
"   has everyone gone home early?
"   did you leave the newspaper at home?
"   were the children sent home from school?
"   should I stay at home today?
"   is the train always so late?
"   have the leaves turned brown?
"   does the door keep slamming?
"   are the waves so high today?
"   has the street been closed to traffic?
"   won't you let me have my way?
"   should I change my plans again?
"   was the sign taken down?
"   did the bank refuse the check?
"   has the dress faded so much?
"   is the party to be postponed?

195.   *When*

When will there be another meeting?
"   does the baseball season open?
"   can we have a game of bridge?
"   will you finish reading the book?
"   is the rainy season?
"   shall we leave for our vacation?
"   did Washington cross the Delaware?
"   were the trees cut down?

When was World War II begun?
" are you going to the football game?
" ought the lawn to be mowed?
" was the grass cut last?
" will the apartment be vacated?
" must the work be finished?
" does the fall term of college begin?
" are you coming to see us again?
" can I expect a reply to my telegram?
" ought we to start the furnace fire?
" will you go with me to the country?
" shall I expect you for dinner?
" would we find them at home?
" will the apple trees be in bloom?
" shall I call for you?
" do the children go back to school?
" will the fruit trees be in bloom?
" did Washington cross the Delaware?
" was the telephone invented?
" shall I see you again?
" do the children go to camp?
" are you taking a vacation?
" were you in the West the last time?
" does the store open in the morning?
" should I start to the office?
" must I get up in the morning?
" was your letter mailed?
" can I expect to see you again?
" will warm weather come?
" should I ask for an interview?
" do the plants have to be brought indoors?
" are you going to build your new house?

196.   *Where*

Where have you been all this time?

"   can I find someone to help me?

"   has the car been parked?

"   would you like to go for dinner?

"   did you go to school?

"   do you want the roses planted?

"   does this road take us?

"   can I rent the latest books to read?

"   is the nearest Post Office?

"   are we going for the picnic?

"   shall I go to get fresh fruit?

"   can we see a good show?

"   is the principal's office?

"   shall we hold the next meeting?

"   did you find such a pretty picture?

"   is your country place?

"   have you put the morning paper?

"   must I put the flowers for the night?

"   may I hang my coat and hat?

"   would you like to be right now?

"   shall I leave the package for you?

"   can I mail my letters?

"   has everyone gone?

"   would you like to spend the evening?

"   is the picture being shown?

"   in the world have you been?

"   are we to have our lunch?

"   was the first city in the United States founded?

"   did you get that hat?

"   is the Old Dominion?

"   shall I spend the holidays?

Where can we have peace and quiet?
" should we go on Sunday?
" will I find the latest book?
" has the car been parked?
" did you find the matching furniture?
" is the nearest swimming pool?
" can we see the sailboats on the bay?
" would you like to go from here?
" will the furniture look best?

197. *Which*

Which house do you live in?
" telephone has an amplifier?
" bank will cash my check?
" theater has the best show?
" hearing aid is the strongest?
" necktie shall I wear today?
" pen is the best for the work?
" room would you like for your own?
" airplane had the best chance to win?
" school has the most students?
" newspaper do you read each day?
" store is best for household furnishings?
" program was the most interesting?
" room will you rent to me?
" bus am I to take at the corner?
" umbrella do you want for your birthday?
" train do you take in the morning?
" documents should I destroy?
" work ought I to do first?
" furniture goes into this room?
" is your favorite store in town?
" route shall I take going West?

Which subject do you like best at school?
    "   town has the best schools?
    "   lamp gives the better light?
    "   flower is the most beautiful?
    "   room has the best light?
    "   hospital is the best?
    "   boat are you going to take?
    "   airline shall I take to California?
    "   day will suit you best?
    "   house is for rent?
    "   way do we go from here?
    "   of these packages belongs to you?
    "   horse do you think will win the race?
    "   school has the best teacher?
    "   room has the best light?
    "   club do you belong to?
    "   do you like better, the mountains or seashore?
    "   child made the highest marks?
    "   place is best for the piano?
    "   library is best for research work?

198.   *Who*

Who has half a dollar to lend me?
    "   has been left in charge of the office?
    "   was in the house last?
    "   am I to room with?
    "   will be our next President?
    "   might have the information we want?
    "   were the people I just met?
    "   would like fried chicken for dinner?
    "   should be the one to tell the news?
    "   are on the committee?
    "   will arrange the flowers in church?

Who was chosen for the position?
"   do those people think they are?
"   had the highest average for the year?
"   has been left in charge of the office?
"   can get away for the afternoon?
"   must assume the responsibility?
"   does the baby look like?
"   was at the house last night?
"   does the housework for the family?
"   is to pilot the plane?
"   bought the tickets for the trip?
"   followed us on the road?
"   published the book?
"   passed us in the car?
"   did you see about the meeting?
"   was appointed chairman?
"   is the author of the book you are reading?
"   will go downtown with me?
"   taught you to drive a car?
"   put the car in the garage?
"   has volunteered to help us?
"   will sign the form letter?
"   wrote the article for the newspaper?
"   are you bringing home for dinner?
"   did you say is coming with you?
"   was the last one out of the house?
"   can help me with the chores?
"   started the fire in the living room?
"   mowed the lawn this afternoon?

199.   *Why With All Negative Contractions*

Why haven't my groceries been delivered?
"   "   I received my bank statement?

Why haven't they sent us any word?
" hasn't the clock been wound?
" " she washed the dishes?
" " the law been enforced?
" hadn't you provided a spare tire?
" " the sign been put up?
" isn't he improving more rapidly?
" " she going to be married?
" " there more light in the room?
" wasn't a policeman at the corner?
" " the laundry called for?
" " the mail delivered to the house?
" weren't we met at the station?
" " you more tactful?
" won't the children behave?
" " the ice cream get hard?
" " the cream whip?
" wouldn't the motor boat go?
" " you answer my questions?
" shouldn't I drive through that street?
" " we tell the family?
" don't you show a little more interest?
" " you like the music?
" doesn't she come to see us?
" " the train stop at this station?
" didn't you close the windows before it rained?
" " we think of that ourselves?
" can't you leave me alone?
" " the wires be repaired at once?
" couldn't she use her voice?
" mustn't I speak out loud?
" " we ever come here again?

200. *Pronouns With Contractions*

I'm thinking of going South.

" through for the day.

I'll meet you on the 5:45 train.

" see the thing through.

" never speak to him again!

I'd just gone out when you came in.

" be ashamed of myself if I did that.

I've lived here all my life.

" never heard of such a thing.

" promised to meet her this evening.

He's a jolly good fellow.

" a born leader.

" an authority on the subject.

He'll graduate from college in June.

" be here in a minute.

He'd take a chance any day.

" make a good comedian.

She's a dead game sport.

" just the one for the place.

She'll never make that train.

" help in any way she can.

She'd do well if she would try.

" look well in that dress.

We're anxious to go home for Christmas.

" almost home now.

We'll let you know tomorrow.

" have to try something else.

We'd like you to have lunch with us.

" spent all our money before we knew it.

We've a few minutes left before train time.

" come over to say good bye.

You're the right person for the job.

   "   just the person I wanted to see.

You'll hear from me in the morning.

   "   meet a lot of interesting people.

You'd enjoy the movie.

   "   better come with us.

You've been away a long time.

   "   never looked so well in your life.

They're coming here for supper.

   "   taking part in the concert.

They'd rather play baseball than eat.

   "   signed the papers before we arrived.

They've made a wise decision.

   "   shown good judgment.

201.   *Auxiliary Verbs With All Pronouns*

Have I ever met you before?

   "   you called the number?

   "   they started home yet?

   "   we enough gasoline for the trip?

Has he applied for the position?

   "   she ever been abroad?

   "   it been raining here?

Had I known it I would have gone home.

   "   you been in Paris before?

   "   he read the morning paper?

   "   she promised to come back?

   "   it cleared when you left?

   "   they finished the examination?

Am I making you nervous?

   "   I in the way?

   "   I too early?

   "   I dressed properly for dinner?

Is she alone in the house?

" he president of the company?

" it too late to change my mind?

Are we on time?

"   you a good bridge player?

"   they still talking?

Was he at the office on time?

"   she a kindergarten teacher?

"   it just what you wanted?

Were you talking to me?

"   they prepared to fill the orders?

"   we supposed to be there early?

Will I have time to go home for lunch?

"   you pour tea for me?

"   she get to the train in time?

"   they ever get through talking?

"   it be clear tomorrow?

"   he drive us home?

Would he take a job like that?

"   it look well in this room?

"   they pass us by?

"   she tell us what to do?

"   I have time to change my dress?

Shall we sit by the fire?

"   he be asked to go with us?

"   they be included in the party?

"   I phone you tomorrow?

Should we serve tea or coffee?

"   he have spoken to them?

"   I look over the ground again?

Do you care to have me read aloud?

" they always come late?

" I look as if I had gained weight?

Did they deliver the telegram promptly?
" you ever see such luck!
" it look just right to you?
" he pilot the plane?
" she ask for information?
Does he look like his father?
" it always rain on Sunday?
" she have a permanent wave?
May I speak to you for a minute?
" we join the party?
" he be allowed to speak?
Might I ask a question?
" we help you?
Can she play the organ?
" I do anything for you?
" they beat that record?
" he swim across the lake?
" it be possible that the storm is over?
" we use the tennis courts now?

202.   *Negative Contractions With All Pronouns*

Haven't I see you somewhere?
" you had enough sleep?
" we enough coal for the winter?
" they been here before?
Hasn't it been warm today!
" she an automobile license for this state?
" he telephoned you before?
Hadn't I better ring off?
" they driven over the road before?
" we better go by airplane?
" it made any impression on them?

Hadn't he better try other work?

"   you ever heard the opera?

Isn't he active for his years?

" it where I put it?

" she a fine looking woman?

Aren't you unusually well this summer?

"   they living on the farm?

"   we gay!

"   her clothes becoming!

"   his stories well written!

Wasn't it too bad the rain spoiled our fun?

"   she pleased with the present?

"   he looking well when you saw him last?

"   our play a success?

Weren't you free to do as you pleased?

"   they all skilled musicians?

"   we to be there at five o'clock?

"   her rooms attractive?

"   his friends pleasant?

"   your proofs any good?

Won't you promise never to do it again?

"   she make any reduction in the price?

"   he get into trouble about the broken lease?

Wouldn't it be better to go back now?

"   you like to do something frivolous?

"   she be surprised to see us?

"   her teacher excuse her from the class?

"   his place be kept for him?

"   they rehearse the play?

Shan't I be able to drive fast on the road?

"   we serve dinner now?

"   she change places with me?

"   they take the family along?

Shouldn't we make reservations early?
"   he go away for a few weeks?
"   they be able to dock the boat?
"   I play golf?
"   she have consulted me first?
Don't you agree with me?
"   they like their new home?
"   we leave before nine in the morning?
Doesn't it beat all!
"   she set a rapid pace!
"   he like roast beef?
Didn't I tell you so?
"   it take a long time to drive downtown?
"   she look lovely?
"   they order dinner for us?
"   you pass me on the street?
"   we have a good time!
Mightn't I try that, too?
"   it be the better way out?
"   he open the window?
"   we appeal to the Red Cross?
Can't you look out for yourself?
"   I have an afternoon off?
"   he walk on snowshoes?
"   they hear us talking?
"   we compromise?
"   it be done better than that?
Couldn't I do that for you?
"   they come some other time?
"   we make the sandwiches now?
"   he mend the chair?
"   she make an apple pie?
Mustn't we exceed the speed limit?
"   she leave the house today?

Mustn't he play the piano?

"   they help us with our lessons?

"   it be told?

203.   II. COMMON PHRASES

1. We are going to town one day next week.   2. I got up at dawn this morning.   3. We went out on the river at sunset. 4. We got home late at night.   5. The trip will start early in the morning.   6. You are very early for your lesson.   7. We were on the road at sunrise.   8. We left the house just before daybreak.   9. It began to rain late in the afternoon.   10. Shall we go to the show at midnight?   11. The doorbell rang in the middle of the night.   12. The children came home at noon. 13. We heard the news the next morning.   14. It snowed one morning last week.   15. Many things have happened since then.   16. Some day next week we are going to the country. 17. Will you take a walk with me some morning soon? 18. Let's go shopping some afternoon.   19. Come and see us some evening.   20. Shall we go to the movies some night this week?   21. I want a vacation one of these days.   22. The family will all be home for Thanksgiving.   23. The children have a vacation Easter week.   24. Where shall we go during the Christmas vacation?   25. I hope to get home the day before Christmas.   26. We open our presents on Christmas morning.   27. The children have a party on Christmas Eve. 28. Shall we celebrate on New Year's Eve?   29. We spent a quiet Fourth of July.   30. The flag should be half-mast on Memorial Day.   31. After dinner coffee will be served in the living room.   32. I like to read the paper while eating breakfast.   33. Everyone talked at once during the meal.   34. You should finish the work before lunch.   35. The children like a story at bedtime.   36. The wind blew all night.   37. There were interruptions all day long.   38. The mail is delivered twice a day.   39. We go to the store every other day.

204.

1. It looks like rain today. 2. What did you do yesterday? 3. We are leaving for home tomorrow. 4. We spent last week in camp. 5. What happened week before last? 6. I go to my new job week after next. 7. The weather changed in the middle of the week. 8. The house was closed the first of the week. 9. Everything will be ready the last of the week. 10. We are moving in a few weeks. 11. I saw you several weeks ago. 12. I heard from the family about a week ago. 13. The bill was paid last month. 14. Schools open next month. 15. We don't know what will happen in the future. 16. We mailed the package some time ago. 17. I read the book long ago. 18. The family goes South in the middle of the winter. 19. The house is shut up the beginning of winter. 20. We came back to town the end of the summer. 21. The robins return early in the spring. 22. We are having a late fall. 23. We drove 5,000 miles during vacation. 24. We are leaving home very soon. 25. The weather will change before long. 26. I must have your answer right away. 27. The work will start at once. 28. Spring will be here pretty soon. 29. I'll be ready in a minute. 30. The clock will strike in a few minutes. 31. Shall we take a walk after awhile? 32. I failed to recognize you at first. 33. The mail has come at last. 34. It began to rain not long after we left home. 35. The sun shines all the time here. 36. I was busy every minute of the day. 37. You should take a day off now and then.

205.

1. The mail comes at four o'clock. 2. We are leaving at half past two. 3. We shall have dinner at seven-thirty. 4. Come back at a quarter of eleven. 5. We drove until a quarter past six. 6. The train leaves twelve minutes past three. 7. Bills

will be paid on the first of the month. 8. You should rest on the seventh day. 9. What were you doing last week Monday? 10. The committee will meet next Thursday. 11. The Fourth of March is no longer Inauguration Day. 12. January 20th is Inauguration Day. 13. Washington's Birthday is February 22nd. 14. April 1st is April Fools' Day. 15. Can you change a dollar bill? 16. I haven't a cent for you! 17. Please buy a nickel bar of chocolate. 18. The carfare is a dime. 19. The telephone call cost a quarter. 20. The lunch check was half a dollar. 21. The apron was cheap at 98 cents. 22. The groceries came to three dollars and a half. 23. The bonds pay four per cent interest. 24. The worm was three inches long. 25. The table is 27 inches wide. 26. The material is a yard wide. 27. The man is six feet tall. 28. The lot is one hundred feet wide. 29. The street is a quarter of a mile long. 30. The speed limit is thirty-five miles an hour. 31. The train makes a mile a minute. 32. Potatoes are $1.20 a bushel. 33. We bought half a peck of apples. 34. May we have a half pint of cream? 35. We have only a few pounds of sugar. 36. I want a couple of ounces of pepper. 37. There is a full ton of coal left.

206.

1. We should spend more time out of doors. 2. Have you been outdoors this morning? 3. Please leave the plants outside. 4. There is a bird's nest in the tree. 5. The birds are flitting among the branches. 6. The children swing on the limb of a tree. 7. We had our picnic lunch on the ground. 8. We put our chairs on the lawn. 9. I saw a rabbit in the bushes. 10. The children are hiding behind the hedge. 11. There is a sandbox in the back yard. 12. The chickens are in the garden. 13. The car is parked in front of the house. 14. There is an apartment on top of the building. 15. The

horse is in the stable. 16. I will meet you at the spring. 17. There is a bucket by the well. 18. We drove through the gate into the yard. 19. You must keep inside the fence. 20. Vines grow over the fence. 21. The cows are waiting at the bars. 22. We sat on the stone wall in the sun. 23. The train is on the bridge. 24. The boat cannot go under the bridge. 25. There is too much noise in the court. 26. How many cars were on the road? 27. We planted trees along the driveway. 28. Everyone seems to be on the street today. 29. The stores on the Avenue are closed. 30. My friends live across the street. 31. You must not put boxes on the sidewalk. 32. We walked along the path in the woods. 33. I like to travel on the railroad. 34. The men walk along the railroad to work. 35. The house is near the trolley tracks. 36. There are wild flowers in the woods. 37. The spring is full of leaves. 38. The vine is covered with blossoms. 39. Wait for me in the shade of the tree. 40. I spent an hour in the sunshine. 41. It was cooler after the storm. 42. The workmen eat their lunch under the trees. 43. The apples in the orchard are ripe. 44. The ground under the apple trees is covered with apples. 45. We spent the summer on the farm. 46. There are fine farms in the valley. 47. We are going to the brook to fish.

207.

1. We sit on the porch in the evening. 2. There are chairs on the piazza. 3. The children are playing on the veranda. 4. We sat on the steps. 5. Someone is at the door. 6. Who is in the house? 7. How many people are in the room? 8. Company is in the parlor. 9. I spent the afternoon in the Library. 10. The family are in the living room. 11. The refrigerator is in the kitchen. 12. No one is in the sewing room. 13. Who is in the bedroom? 14. The furnace is in the cellar. 15. We put the old furniture in the attic. 16. The trunks are in the

storeroom. 17. Who will sleep in the spare room? 18. The baby sleeps in the nursery. 19. Please put the dishes on the table. 20. You will find the book in the bookcase. 21. Pencils and paper are in the drawer. 22. Don't leave your book on the chair. 23. I stood at the window to watch the crowd. 24. There is a pad under the rug. 25. You shouldn't put your feet on the desk! 26. The music is on the piano. 27. Why don't you take a nap on the couch? 28. Three people can sit on the sofa. 29. The umbrella is behind the door. 30. There is dust behind the picture. 31. The spool of thread rolled under the bed. 32. The comb and brush are on the bureau. 33. The towels are in the linen closet. 34. I can't reach the top shelf. 35. Who is downstairs? 36. The bedrooms are upstairs. 37. There is a window on the stair landing. 38. Don't lean too far over the banister. 39. Wait for me in the hall. 40. The dishes are in the cupboard. 41. The clothes are in the closet. 42. There is a spider's web across the window. 43. Put the scraps in the waste basket. 44. There is a picture on the wall. 45. The fire makes shadows on the ceiling. 46. I like to sit on the floor. 47. I put the flowers in the bath tub. 48. Wash your hands in the basin. 49. The tooth paste is in the medicine cabinet. 50. The curtains should be washed. 51. The books are on the library table. 52. Please pull down the shades. 53. You should light the gas in the oven. 54. You will have to turn up the gas. 55. It is time to turn on the lights. 56. Please raise the window. 57. Open the window for some fresh air. 58. You should lower the window from the top. 59. Shut the window before it rains. 60. I wish you would close the window. 61. I'll have to put the window down.

208.

1. Breakfast is ready. 2. The family are at the breakfast table. 3. Will you have an orange or a banana? 4. I prefer

grapefruit for breakfast. 5. Some people like prunes better. 6. We had peaches and cream for dessert. 7. The baked apples were delicious. 8. The strawberry shortcake was just right. 9. We had blueberry pie and ice cream. 10. Currant jelly goes well with chicken. 11. Do you want hot or cold cereal? 12. Will you have sugar and cream on your oatmeal? 13. The hot muffins are ready. 14. We have buttered toast and tea in the afternoon. 15. Men like bacon and eggs for breakfast. 16. How about ham and eggs?. 17. How long shall I boil your eggs? 18. Scrambled eggs are better. 19. The invalid should have poached eggs on toast. 20. Do you like fish cakes for breakfast? 21. I want a cup of coffee the first thing in the morning. 22. Do you drink tea for breakfast? 23. I prefer a glass of milk. 24. We have lunch at twelve-thirty. 25. Will you have breaded lamb chops? 26. We served cold chicken for lunch. 27. We had potato salad at the picnic. 28. The restaurant makes good lobster salad. 29. Would you rather have lobster à la Newburgh? 30. We had ice cream and assorted cakes at the party. 31. Will you have iced tea or iced coffee? 32. We have ice-cold buttermilk. 33. Dinner is being served. 34. I like oyster stew on a cold day. 35. Do you like broiled bluefish? 36. We had oysters on the half shell. 37. Will you have your roast beef rare or well done? 38. The roast chicken was stuffed with oyster dressing. 39. We had roast lamb for Sunday dinner. 40. The broiled lamb chops were just right. 41. There were pork chops and apple sauce. 42. Will you have mashed or French fried potatoes? 43. I never ate better macaroni and cheese. 44. The string beans were cooked just long enough. 45. The corn on the cob had just been picked. 46. You forgot the pepper and salt. 47. We had pumpkin pie for dinner. 48. The mince pie was too rich for me. 49. How would you like lemon pie? 50. Rice pudding is a wholesome dessert. 51. Chocolate pudding is

always a favorite. 52. Where can I buy chocolate éclairs?
53. We had nuts, raisins, and black coffee for the last course.

209.

1. The railroad fare to Washington is $10.50. 2. A round
trip would cost only $18. 3. The fare on the bus is 13 cents, or
3 tokens for 35 cents. 4. You can buy a weekly pass for $1.75.
5. It would cost $15 to go by airplane. 6. The limousine costs
$1 to the Airport. 7. If you go first class on the train a lower
berth will be $3.50. 8. There is a 15 per cent tax on all tickets.
9. The taxi fare was $1.85 from the station. 10. The fare to
Chicago is $44.35 by coach. 11. First class fare to Buffalo is
$43.90. 12. The new shoes cost $17.95. 13. For $10.95 you can
buy a pair of walking shoes. 14. They charged $4.50 for the
bedroom slippers. 15. Nylon hose were sold for $1.55 a pair.
16. Dresses for $19.95 were advertised in today's paper.
17. Cotton house dresses for $6.35 were on sale. 18. The
gabardine suit was sold for $75. 19. There is a sale of men's
two-trouser suits for $65. 20. The bathing suit is cheap at
$12.50. 21. Can you buy a pair of slacks for $10? 22. The
apartment rents for $125 a month. 23. It will take $150 a
month to keep up the place. 24. Our electric bill for the month
was $10.25. 25. Fuel oil costs about eleven cents a gallon.
26. It costs $25 a month to heat the house in cold weather.
27. We pay $5 a week to have the lawn kept in order. 28. Our
new car set us back $3,000. 29. The gas bill is $25 a month.
30. Repairs to the old car cost $77.15. 31. The salary to start
will be $25 a week. 32. The company allows 7 cents a mile
for gas. 33. The President receives a salary of $100,000 a year.
34. A millionaire's income is subject to about seventy per cent
tax. 35. You can deduct 15 per cent of your income for
benevolences. 36. His income tax amounted to $679.53.